Side-Effect

Side-Effect

Raymond Hawkey

NEW ENGLISH LIBRARY/TIMES MIRROR

First published in Great Britain in 1979 by Jonathan Cape Ltd

©1979 by Raymond Hawkey

First NEL Paperback Edition March 1980

NEL Books are published by
New English Library from
Barnard's Inn, Holborn,
London ECIN 2JR.
Made and printed in Great Britain by
William Collins Sons & Co Ltd, Glasgow

Typeset by Parker Typesetting Services

45004572 2

Side-effect, an effect, often undesirable,
additional to the effect sought.

Chambers's Twentieth Century Dictionary

Acknowledgments

I would like to thank the following people for the advice they so generously gave me during the writing of *Side-effect*. Without their help (and the help of those who, because of the sensitive nature of their jobs, cannot be thanked publicly), this book might not have been begun, much less finished. If mistakes have been made, the fault is mine, not theirs.

Tom Appleton, of De Havilland Aircraft of Canada; Captain Robert L. Cheshire, of the School of Navigation, Plymouth Polytechnic; Eric and Marcelle Clark; Jonathan Clowes; Suzan Deighton, of the British Computer Society Library, London; Ken Denyer; Jeannette Dranoff; Shirley Dutton; Dr Richard B. Fisher; Neil L. Frank, of the National Hurricane Center, Miami; Tom Huff; Dr John Jenkins, of the Imperial College of Science and Technology, London; William C. Jordan and Lorraine G. Winchester, of WCJ Inc., Los Angeles; Dr E. F. Lobl; Mabel Moore, of St Peter's Hospital, London; John Prizeman; Jean Robinson, of the Patients' Association, London; Harold Ryder; Dr John Sachs, of the Tissue Immunology Unit, the London Hospital; Patrick Tilley; Pierre-André Tilley.

Lastly, I would like to thank Roger Bingham – my co-author on *Wild Card* – for all that he has done to make this book possible. Although himself engaged in writing a biography of Dr Jacob Bronowski, he never once failed to respond (sometimes from the other side of the world) to my many cries for help on finding myself lost in the denser thickets of science and technology.

Part One

You can't make omelets without breaking eggs.
Brewer's Dictionary of Phrase and Fable

1

Clair Tennant turned to face her dressing-table mirror and gathered up her fair, shoulder-length hair, trying to imagine how it would look cut short. Probably okay, she decided, turning her head one way and then the other. She had the features for it, and short hair would show off her long, slender neck to good effect, as well as being cooler – much cooler.

After a witheringly cold winter and a wet, blustery spring, the sudden arrival of fine weather had, at first, been exhilarating. London had taken on an almost carnival atmosphere, and Clair, soon tanned the colour of burnt sugar, had rediscovered the pleasures of driving barefoot in an open car, dining on candle-lit terraces overlooking the river, and making love on top of, instead of between, the sheets.

But as one cloudless, windless day followed another, the heat – in a city where air-conditioners are still almost a collector's item – had become stifling. Soon she had begun to find it difficult to stay awake during the day, and even harder to get to sleep at night. Her work as a freelance graphic designer suffered, and hoping to ease the tension that this produced she had begun smoking again, which depressed still further her heat-jaded appetite. Already slim, she had begun to lose weight, and seemed never to be without a headache.

And then, uncharacteristically, she had become irritable; so irritable that Michael Fitzpatrick, the science reporter with whom she lived, had suggested that she might be suffering from pre-menstrual tension. 'That,' she had snapped, 'is a typically male chauvinist remark!'

Mike had reminded her that for several weeks *he* had been the one who had done most of the shopping, cooking and cleaning, whereupon she had accused him of doing it only in order to make her feel guilty. He had told her she was being absurd, and although knowing this to be true, she had been indignant. 'So now I'm being absurd, am I?' she had cried. 'Well, if that's what you think, the sooner I get to hell out of here the better!'

She refused to admit that her outburst had been to do with

anything other than overwork, but she had made her peace with Mike. However, the incident had set her worrying. It was true that her irritability had been exacerbated by an unusually high level of pre-menstrual tension, but she was certain it had not been caused by it. She had never had problems of that sort before, and anyway, she'd been feeling lousy long before the onset of her period. Neither did she believe that it was anything to do with the weather; in the past she'd always thrived on the heat. No, there was, she decided, definitely something the matter with her, and when her own doctor had failed to discover what it was she had made an appointment to be examined at the Institute of Preventive Medicine, a multiphasic health screening unit in North London.

However, having once made the appointment, she began to wonder *why* she had made it. Had her widowed mother's death from cancer eighteen months earlier turned her into a hypochondriac? Was this why she was spending money they could ill afford on a screening she didn't really need? The more she thought about it, the more convinced she had become that this was the answer. It explained why she had decided to go to the Institute rather than to the less expensive BUPA Medical Centre (the Institute's tests were, she had read somewhere, the more searching of the two), and why she had mentioned none of it to Mike.

Annoyed with herself for having been so foolish, she glanced at her watch and wondered whether she couldn't, even now, call the Institute and make an excuse for having to cancel. She decided she just couldn't – it was too short notice.

What the hell! she thought, tucking her hair behind her ears; everyone ought to have a check-up once in a while. She began massaging her face with moisturizing cream. And anyway, now that she was feeling so much better, it would be no great hardship to take on one extra job next month in order to pay for the screening.

Beside her was a transistor radio, and as soon as she heard the 8 a.m. time signal she called out: 'Darling, the news!'

The door of the adjoining bathroom opened and Mike appeared, wet from the shower and with a towel wrapped around his middle. He had the lean, muscular body of a man

10

who, while not being obsessed with physical perfection, nevertheless took pains to keep himself in good trim; a handsome face framed by black, curly hair that he was rubbing vigorously with a second towel, and good-humoured, intelligent grey eyes – eyes which did much to offset the faintly disturbing Spanish cast to his features that is typical of a certain strain of Irishman.

'But first, the President's Firearms Control Bill,' said the newsreader, having come to the end of the headlines. Mike stopped towelling his hair and leaned against the door-frame, listening with professional interest. 'This was how millions of Americans heard the President make his historic announcement on coast-to-coast television last night.'

'Good evening,' he began, in the flat, slightly sibilant Southern accent which had made him the easiest president to mimic since John F. Kennedy. 'By now, many of you will have seen the FBI's Annual Uniform Crime Report, and, like, me, will have been dismayed to learn that the level of serious crime in our country has increased 20 per cent over last year.

'More disturbing still, you will have learned of the greatly increased use made of firearms during the commission of crimes of violence – a staggering 140 per cent rise over the previous year.

'For many years now, opinion polls have shown the overwhelming majority of you to be in favour of stricter gun-control laws. But always this wish has been subverted by a small but highly organized minority determined to maintain the status quo at whatever the price in human suffering.

'This, my friends, is a situation which we cannot – must not – allow to continue.

'It is for this reason that I, after the August recess, intend to lay before Congress a bill requiring the federal registration of all firearms and the licensing of all who possess them.'

Mike and Clair exchanged sympathetic glances in the dressing-table mirror. It had been a long time since he'd had a worthwhile assignment, and although both knew that tomorrow's papers would be full of follow-up pieces about the Firearms Control Bill, they also knew that with no obvious scientific angle to the story, none of them was likely to come his way.

11

With a forlorn shrug, he returned to the bathroom, resigned to the prospect of yet another day spent cobbling together pieces about the heatwave.

After switching off the radio, Clair crossed to the wardrobe. She didn't feel in the mood for a dress, and yet it was far too hot for jeans. In the end she decided on her sand-coloured cotton culottes and jacket, and a brown T-shirt. She dressed, slipped into a pair of open-toe sandals and went clattering down the wrought-iron spiral staircase to the main room. Painted white throughout, the sun-filled room contained Clair's drawing table, plan-chest and apple-green filing cabinets, a pair of corduroy-covered settees and a dining table and chairs. There were three enormous windows in one wall, and, on the facing wall, shelves holding books and the early brass-and-mahogany scientific instruments Mike had begun collecting when a student at University College. Hanging above the shelves were some of the things which had caught Clair's eye at one time or another – dried flowers and pieces of driftwood, Victorian printers' specimen sheets and music-hall posters, a stuffed pike in a glass case and a big schoolroom clock that had cost more to set going than to buy.

After picking up the newspapers and mail, she went into the kitchen and began preparing breakfast.

As the coffee began to perk, she heard Mike coming down the stairs. She put aside the letter she had been reading, intending to tell him where she was going and why. But as she opened her mouth to speak, the telephone began to ring. It was the news editor of the mass-circulation daily for which Mike worked. 'It's Ted,' she said, handing him the phone. She pulled the plug out of the percolator and began pouring coffee. Something seemed to have happened that was going to take Mike away from London, but she couldn't make out what or where. She put cream and sugar into one of the mugs and took it across to him.

Mike smiled his thanks and took a sip of the coffee. 'And there'll definitely be a seat on the eleven o'clock flight?' she heard him ask. He spoke softly and with only a trace of a Dublin accent. 'Okay, I'll check with you as soon as I arrive.'

He slammed down the phone and stood up. 'Sod it! You

know what they want me to do now? They only want me to go to *Belfast*!'

'Belfast?' Clair opened the refrigerator and took out eggs and milk. 'Why Belfast?'

'Our man there crashed his car earlier this morning. They want me to take over till the poor bugger's out of hospital.'

'Until he's out of *hospital*? Was he badly hurt?'

Mike began rolling down the sleeves of his shirt. 'Bad enough. They seem to think he'll be in for at least ten days.'

'Oh, *no*!' A note of annoyance had crept into Clair's voice. 'But that means we'll have to cancel dinner with John and Judy for a second time!'

'You can have them over without me being here, can't you?'

'It wouldn't be the same.' Clair began breaking eggs into a bowl. 'And anyway, why does it have to be you who goes?'

'They're short-staffed because of the holidays, and they know I know the place. Anyway, I'm not exactly earning my keep over here at the moment.' Mike paused to look at his watch. 'Jesus!' he cried, snatching up his jacket. 'I'm going to have to do something about getting packed!'

'Do you want me to do it for you?' she asked, wiping her hands on a paper towel.

Mike gulped down the remains of his coffee and shook his head. 'Thanks all the same. Hey, but listen, love,' he said, taking the mug across to the sink, 'if you could try to get me a cab, that would be great.'

Within fifteen minutes Mike had packed and a taxi had arrived to take him to London Airport. They kissed goodbye, and feeling suddenly very alone, Clair went back inside the flat to wait until it was time for her to leave.

2

Clair completed the last of her tests at the Institute of Preventive Medicine at 1.30 in the afternoon. In New York it was 8.30 in the morning, and the limousine which had brought Frank Mancini from his Sutton Place mansion had just pulled up alongside the entrance to the Eldorado Tower.

Accompanied by two bodyguards wearing Secret Service-style earpieces and sleeve microphones, Mancini entered the bustling lobby and breasted his way through to the executive elevator. He was a big, powerfully built man with crew-cut greying hair, a stubborn, deeply lined face and heavily lidded eyes; a man who, in some strange way, seemed surrounded by a force field of malevolent energy.

'Welcome back, Mr Mancini,' said the porter, throwing him a salute. 'How're you feeling?'

'Terrific.' Mancini swept past him into the car and turned. 'Now let's get this thing rolling, huh?' he growled.

'Yessir, Mr Mancini. Right away.'

The porter released the hold button and the doors snapped shut. The men in the elevator stood silently watching the floor numbers flick on and off, until, at 60, there was a ping and the doors opened on to the thickly carpeted vestibule of the executive suite.

Warned by the security guard in the lobby that Mancini was on his way up, his secretary was there to meet him.

'Okay, where are they?' he demanded, before the girl had a chance to begin her carefully rehearsed welcome-back speech.

'Finishing breakfast in the executive dining-room,' she replied, almost having to run to keep up with him.

'Tell them to get their asses in here on the double.' Mancini strode past a plinth supporting a bronze bust of Ernest Hemingway and threw open the double doors to his office. 'Then call Dr Zieminski and have him stop by at the house later this evening.'

The room he entered was huge, and had been decorated in a style which, like the faded jeans and unbuttoned patchwork

14

denim shirt he was wearing, was intended to leave no one in any doubt that he was a man's man, tough and uncompromising. The walls were clad in teak panels, and lying in front of an enormous stone fireplace was a buffalo-skin rug flanked by a pair of black leather chesterfields. Above the fireplace, along with part of his priceless collection of antique firearms, hung the head of a lion he had shot in East Africa, its glass eyes narrowed menacingly and its mouth open in a silent roar. There was a walnut conference table almost long enough to have landed a light aircraft on, and on the facing wall, trophies of another sort – framed photographs of Mancini with all of the great macho figures of the 1980s.

The son of an immigrant printer from Milan, Mancini had left high school to study chemical engineering at the Polytechnic Institute of Brooklyn. After graduating, he had got a job in the research and development department of a large printing company in Philadelphia, where he had hit upon an idea for printing colour photographs in a way that made them appear three-dimensional. He had resigned, taken out patents on the process and returned to New York, where, with money put up by Mafia contacts quick to realize the commercial potential of a 3-D girlie magazine, he had produced a printed dummy which he named Eldorado. It had proved to be an auspicious title, for not only did photographs of naked girls appear more desirable when seen in three dimensions – so, too, did a vast range of high-priced merchandise. Furniture, hi-fi and sports equipment, cars, clothes, drinks – all could be made to appear highly seductive within the 3-D sections of *Eldorado*, and Madison Avenue was soon clamouring for advertising space.

The first issue of 500,000 copies had sold out almost immediately, but such was the impact of *Eldorado's* 3-D nudes that within a week Mancini was facing over a hundred separate prosecutions for obsenity.

With characteristic chutzpah, he had issued a written undertaking to indemnify any news-stand vendor prosecuted for selling *Eldorado*, at the same time ordering a reprint three times the size of the initial run.

This, too, had sold out almost immediately, and within a year *Eldorado* had come to dominate the young, upper-income

15

male magazine market, selling an average of eight million copies a month in the United States alone.

There had been no stopping him, and within a few years he owned not only magazines, but newspapers, television and radio stations, and a film distribution and production company.

A right-wing Republican, Mancini had lost no time in using his empire as a stick with which to beat the Democratic Administration. At first they had been no more than irritated. But as Mancini began to pile on the pressure, irritation had turned to anger, anger to rage. Soon, he found himself coming under pressure from the Administration. Challenges against his ownership of television stations in three States had been filed with the Federal Communications Commission; he had been investigated by the Intelligence Division of the Internal Revenue Service; charged with violating Securities and Exchange rules regarding the sale of stock, and misuse of the Mails.

And then, while on honeymoon with his third wife in Mexico, he had been served with a subpoena to appear before a Senate Committee to Investigate Organized Crime.

Although it was one of Mancini's boasts that he had never had a day's illness in his life, unknown to him, cholesterol had begun to encrust the linings of the two tree-like bunches of arteries responsible for nourishing his constantly overworked heart. Shortly after taking off for Washington, a clot (caused by a complex biochemical interaction between blood platelets and deposits of cholesterol) had suddenly blocked his upper right coronary artery, depriving part of his heart of the oxygen and nutrients needed to sustain it.

At first, Mancini had thought the pain in his chest was nothing more than indigestion brought on by a stressful, hastily eaten dinner of *chile verde* and *frijoles*, but as the pain spread across to his left shoulder and down his arm, the terrible truth had dawned on him – he had suffered a cardiac infarction.

The pilot had diverted to Houston, where, with his heart now beginning to fibrillate, Mancini was rushed to the Texas Medical Center.

Following a period in an intensive-care unit, he had been subjected to a battery of tests which revealed that the infarction had destroyed part of his heart. Moreover, the nature of the damage was such as to rule him out as a candidate for a coronary bypass. Although the doctors had saved his life, there was little more that they could do for him; from now on, his fate would largely be in his own hands.

Apparently reconciled to the idea of living the life of a semi-invalid, he returned to New York, replaced his French chef with a dietitian, converted the squash court of his mansion into a fully equipped cardiovascular clinic and announced his retirement. In future, said the statement, he would interest himself only in long-term policy decisions.

Everything had gone well until the previous evening, when the President's address to the nation had so enraged him that he had almost had another heart attack.

'Gentlemen, I've called you together today to discuss what attitude we as a corporation should take to the proposed gun-control legislation,' Mancini began, as soon as his chiefs of staff had assembled in his office. 'So, what do you think? Is tighter gun control a good or a bad thing?' He looked around the crowded conference table. 'Bill, what about you?'

Bill Brackman, who was the editor of one of Mancini's West Coast dailies, had been taking a lot of flak from New York recently. Only a week earlier, Mancini had telexed him a memo complaining about his editorial judgment that had almost peeled the veneer off Brackman's desk. This, however, was his chance to redeem himself in his boss's eyes.

'Bad!' he said, confident that that was the answer expected of him. 'Apart from anything else, it would be a violation of the Second Amendment.'

'The Second Amendment only guarantees a State's right to maintain an armed militia,' said Mancini blandly. 'It has nothing to do with the *private* possession of firearms.'

Brackman blew out his cheeks dismissively. 'I know that's one of the arguments always advanced by proponents of tighter gun control,' he said, thinking Mancini was playing devil's advocate. 'However, I still believe we can build a pretty powerful case that such legislation would be unconstitutional.'

'Sure we can, but *should* we?'

Brackman stole a glance at the guns displayed on the fire-

17

place wall. 'Yes, I think we should,' he said, with even greater confidence.

'Why?'

'Why?' Brackman shifted uneasily in his seat. 'Well, for one thing, it would sure put the President's nose out of joint!'

Mancini began drumming his fingers on the table. 'You think so?'

'Well yes I do, Mr Mancini,' he replied, hoping it wasn't apparent that his mouth had suddenly gone as dry as the Mojave Desert. 'Don't you?'

'No, I don't,' Mancini said flatly. 'I think building a case *against* tighter gun control is just what that bastard would like us to do.'

'Okay, so let me ask you another question. Why do you think he waited until the final year of his second term before reopening this particular can of worms?'

'I, uh . . .' Brackman looked anxiously around the table, but the others were as careful not to catch his eye as they were Mancini's. 'Well, I guess he figured he needed things to have gotten really bad out on the streets before he'd have a chance of getting the legislation on to the statute book . . .'

Mancini's drumming, which had been building to a climax, stopped abruptly. '*Bullshit!*' he said savagely. 'He knows he hasn't got a snowball's chance in hell of getting it on to the statute book! And I'll tell you something else: the sonuvabitch doesn't even want to get it on to the statute book! This has nothing to do with gun control; it's to do with getting Forrestal into the goddamned White House when it's his time to step down!'

'The Attorney-*General*?' Brackman stared at him blankly. 'In the *White* House?'

'Who else? Forrestal's closer to the President than anybody else in his cabinet. He's young, he's ambitious, he's rich; and when he wants to, the cold-assed sonuvabitch can charm the feathers off a goose.' Mancini shrugged. 'What else does a presidential candidate need?'

'Okay, but how does *not* getting the Bill through help?'

Mancini began playing with the shark's tooth pendant he wore around his neck. 'Listen, for the past fifty years opinion polls have shown the public to be in favour of tighter gun control, right? And what happened? Nothing! And why didn't it? Because the gun lobby – what he called that "highly organized minority" – made damned sure it didn't.

'Last night I talked to the guys at the National Rifle Association and the Shooting Sports Foundation, and they're getting ready to mount one of the most intensive lobby campaigns to have hit Capitol Hill since before Prohibition.

'So, yet again, it looks as if legislation that 75, maybe even 80, per cent of the American people want will get blocked. Except *this* time they're not just going to shrug their shoulders and forget it. This time – with it getting like a target range down there on the streets – they're going to be good and pissed off. Suddenly Forrestal's going to have himself one hell of an issue with which to fight the election. Suddenly he's going to be St George, the public the damsel in distress, and the goddamned gun lobby the dragon!

'Which is why, gentlemen, we're going to pull every trick in the book to see that the Bill goes through, and goes through in its entirety. If we succeed, Forrestal's going to find himself in the same kind of shit Bobby Kennedy found *him*self in after Johnson withdrew from the '68 election – a candidate without an issue.'

The Deputy Vice-President of the Eldorado Corporation began to shake his head gravely. 'Frank, I'm worried. Very worried. Not about your political analysis – that's entirely plausible. And I'm not worried about us supporting tighter gun control in the *East*. In the East, it'll go down like a dozen Cape Cod oysters.

'But in the South and Southwest, and in the Midwest—' he drew in his breath sharply '—Jesus H. *Christ*, that's a very different ballgame! Get the pitch wrong there, and we're going to find ourselves losing readers and advertising revenue so fast we won't know what's hit us!'

Mancini nodded. 'That's why I intend to co-ordinate the campaign personally.'

'*Personally*?' The Deputy Vice-President looked thunderstruck. 'But Frank baby, come the Fall, this'll have gotten to be the toughest, fastest game in town . . .'

'And you figure that with my ticker the way it is, I'm not going to be able to handle it, right?' Mancini scratched the back of one of his large, liver-spotted hands. 'Well, the other item of news I've got for you is that by the Fall I intend being back in action full time – fitter than ever before!'

3

'Abe,' said Mancini, laying aside the bundle of page proofs he had brought back from the office, 'Abe, I want you to fix for me to have a heart transplant.'

Abraham Zieminski sighed. A small, dapper man with a mournful face and hair like rusted wire-wool, he had been Mancini's doctor for a long time. Too long. In fact just before Mancini had had his heart attack, Zieminski had begun to feel so much like the dormouse at the Mad Hatter's tea-party that he had seriously considered telling him to go to hell and find himself another doctor.

'I see,' he said, gathering up the cards with which he had been playing solitaire. 'A brain transplant, *this* I could understand,' he continued, turning to an imaginary audience. 'But a *heart* transplant?'

Tut-tutting, he reached down into his black medical bag for a stethoscope, and, after getting Mancini to take off his shirt, listened to his heart for a minute. 'Now,' he said, returning to his seat, 'what's all this nonsense about you wanting a transplant?'

For five minutes he listened while Mancini explained what he believed lay behind the President's Firearms Control Bill, and what he intended to do about it.

Zieminski began shaking his head sadly. 'Frank, I know you too well. You've been *waiting* for something like this to happen – praying for it to happen – so you'd have an excuse to go back.'

Mancini crossed to the bar and broke open a bottle of Jack Daniel's. 'I'll tell you something: if I'd had to sit around here for much longer I'd have gone bananas!'

I'm not surprised, thought Zieminski, looking balefully around him. A couple of years earlier Mancini had been told that 1940s Americana was the in-thing, and had begun collecting the moulded plywood furniture, pintables and nickelodeons, old movie posters and tin tradesmen's signs with which the enormous split-level room was now filled.

'Well, it's your life,' he said, as Mancini handed him his

21

drink. 'I can only tell you that if you carry on like you've been carrying on today, the chances are you'll be dead by Christmas.'

Mancini began feeding tokens into the nearest of the nickelodeons. The first disc to drop on to the brilliantly lit turntable was of a group singing in four-part harmony. 'My heart sighs for you,' they began, 'cries for you, dies for you.' He winced; until his illness he hadn't realized just how many references to sighing hearts, crying hearts and dying hearts there were in popular songs.

'It's because I intend carrying on as I've been carrying on today that I want a transplant,' he said, sitting down.

'Not that *again*! Listen, your heart's not good – okay! – but it's not that bad either, praise God. If you'd continue to take life easy, avoid emotional stress, live by the calendar and not the stop-watch—'

'Forget it,' said Mancini, shaking his head. 'In my book that kind of a chickenshit life just isn't worth living. Christ, Abe, after all this time you should know I'm not a guy who can do things by half measures. I want a new heart, and I want it quick.'

Zieminski banged down his glass. 'And where do you propose to go for this new heart of yours?' he asked, suddenly exasperated. 'Macy's basement?' He took out a handkerchief and began mopping up the whisky he had spilled on the occasional table. 'Or do you want that I should give you mine?'

'Knock it off, Abe, I'm being serious.'

'So am I! Frank, you've gotta be out of your *mind*! Listen, having a heart transplant isn't like having a kidney transplant. If a kidney's rejected it's tough, but it's not the end of the world. You simply go back on dialysis and wait for another. But if a *heart*'s rejected, that's it. Curtains.'

Mancini rattled the ice in his glass. 'And what makes you think mine will be rejected?'

'Even with auto-immunization, a lot still are,' Zieminski told him. 'Unlike the kidney, the heart can't be stored outside the human body. If it isn't transplanted more or less directly from donor to recipient, it's useless. So, if the donor dies before they've finished conditioning the recipient's immune response system to tolerate any mismatched antigens – and except in the case of identical twins, the chances are that there will be mis-matched antigens – you have to start using immunosuppressive drugs. And then you're *really* in trouble, because with your immune response system out of action you're wide open to infection. Hell, I've known patients on immunosuppressive drugs who've had their faces eaten away by cold sores!'

'The guy I intend going to doesn't use immunosuppressive drugs,' Mancini announced. 'He doesn't have to. He can fix you up with a perfectly matched heart, or anything else for that matter.'

Zieminski tried not to smile. 'I see,' he said blandly. 'And may one be permitted to ask the name of this miracle-man?'

'He's called Snaith.'

'*Walter* Snaith?' Zieminski's voice rose nearly an octave. 'The one who all the hassle was about a few years back?'

Mancini nodded.

'And you want *me* to refer *you* to Walter Snaith? For a *heart* transplant? Is that what you're saying?'

'Why not?' Mancini eyed him moodily. 'Max Spiegel got *him*self a new heart from Snaith and he's in great shape.

'His latest movie looks like being one of the biggest grossers of all time,' he added, as if it were in some way a tribute to Snaith's skill as a surgeon. '*And* he brought it in under budget and ahead of time!'

Zieminski bumped the side of his head with his hand, like someone trying to re-start a watch that had suddenly stopped. 'But Frank,' he said incredulously, 'it was *your* people who were to blame for Snaith losing his research funds!'

'It was the *Washington Post* which broke the story,' Mancini protested. 'I don't own the *Washington Post*. Or at least not *yet* I don't . . .'

'The *Post*'s story was well balanced and objective. It was your people who worked the whole thing up into a shitstorm! Christ, Frank, some of your papers even carried a cartoon of Snaith as Frankenstein!'

Mancini dismissed the incident with a wave of his hand. 'Snaith's doing all right,' he said, taking a Monte Cristo from a silver humidor enchased with pictures of flying geese. 'He's got himself a very ritzy clinic in Miami and another in the

Bahamas. *And* he's diversified. He's into real estate, microprocessors – you name it.' He peeled the band off the cigar, rolled it into a ball and flicked it into the fireplace. 'Shit, man, we did the sonuvabitch a favour!'

'Did him a favour?' said Zieminski indignantly. 'If you'd been around to do Jenner, or Pasteur, or Lister the same kind of favour, medicine would still be in the Dark Ages!'

Mancini struck a match and began turning the end of the cigar in the flame. 'All we did was report that a lot of people didn't much like what Snaith was into. Isn't that what the media's supposed to be all about?'

'And just what *was* he into?'

'Something to do with—' Mancini waved his hand vaguely. 'I can't remember the details, but it was something to do with test-tube babies . . .' He paused to draw on his cigar, the first he had smoked since his coronary. 'Anyway,' he said, shaking out the match, 'I thought we were talking about me having a heart transplant, not playing twenty questions.'

'You don't know, do you?'

'Of course I don't *know*!' said Mancini irritably. 'How the fuck should I know? I'm a publisher, not a goddamned doctor.'

'Then I'll tell you,' said Zieminski, determined – now that an undreamed-of opportunity had presented itself – to rub Mancini's nose in what his newspapers, television and radio stations had done to Snaith. 'When he was still a surgeon at the Denton Cooley Memorial Hospital, Snaith had an idea,' he began. 'Like all the best ideas, it was essentially very simple. Aware that the only certain way of overcoming the graft-rejection barrier was to use an identical-twin donor, Snaith got to thinking that if he were to take the nucleus from a human egg and replace it with the nucleus from a body cell of someone with – say – a diseased heart, he'd eventually have a genetic replica from which to take a brand-new replacement heart – a heart the patient would in effect have grown himself.'

'By genetic replica, I take it you mean a test-tube baby?'

'Well, yes,' replied Zieminski, warily. 'But one conceived asexually, using an egg taken from a disembodied, laboratory-maintained ovary and grown to term in an artificial womb.'

Mancini nodded. 'And then what?'

'Before the foetus had acquired the capacity to suffer pain, he'd have dissected out the heart, perfused it and boosted its growth rate with hormones, and transplanted it into the patient from whose body cell it had been grown.'

'And what would have happened to the baby afterwards?'

'How do you mean, what would have happened to it afterwards?'

'For Christ's sake, it's a simple enough question!' snapped Mancini. 'What would have happened to the baby after the poor bastard had had its heart removed?'

'It would have been . . .' Zieminski shrugged. 'Well, I guess it would have been terminated.'

'You mean murdered, don't you?'

Zieminski bridled. 'That's unfair! We don't talk about "murdering babies" when we terminate pregnancies – and we terminate tens of thousands every year.'

'Some people do!'

'Some people say the world is flat!'

'All right! But why get into such a contentious neck of the woods? Why not build a mechanical heart?'

'Why scratch your ear with your foot when you've got hands? Look, the heart's a masterpiece of efficiency. It pulses somewhere in the region of forty-five to fifty million times a year. Most rubber begins to crack at around six million pulses. And then there's the problem of how you power a mechanical heart, vary its output, prevent it from damaging the blood . . .' Zieminski dismissed the idea contemptuously. 'But let's get back to the point, which is that if Snaith had been allowed to continue with his work, transplant surgery might have been revolutionized. By now, we might have stopped using immunosuppressive drugs, stopped wasting valuable time with auto-immunization, and stopped cannibalizing the dead for organs. Rejection would have become a thing of the past, and everyone who needed a transplant could have had one.' Zieminski drained his glass, relieved to have at last said what he'd been wanting to say for so long. 'Even *you*!' he added sardonically.

'So, what are you trying to tell me?' demanded Mancini. 'That Snaith won't take me as a patient? Is that what all this has been about?'

Zieminski shrugged. 'I don't know if he will or not. What interests *me* is why you want to become his patient – a man you tarred and feathered and as good as ran out of town?'

'Like I say, because any heart I get from Snaith will be guaranteed proof against rejection.'

'You don't *really* believe that, do you?' Zieminski asked in a pained voice. 'Frank, for chrissake listen to me – there's no way anyone can give such a guarantee!' His tone became more conciliatory. 'All right, I know Snaith has *fewer* rejects than probably any other transplant surgeon in the world. But he still has rejects. And your heart could be one of them.'

Mancini unbuttoned the breast pocket of his shirt and took out a sheet of paper. 'Take a look at that,' he said, unfolding the sheet and passing it to Zieminski. 'Those are the names of some of the people who've had transplants from Snaith. And, like Spiegel, they're all in great shape.'

Zieminski slipped on a pair of wire-rimmed glasses and began reading. 'Is this who I think it is?' he asked, pausing to point at the name of an internationally famous film actress.

'It is.'

'And she's had a *heart* transplant?'

'Fallopian tubes,' Mancini replied. 'She'd been hankering after kids of her own for years, but hadn't wanted them conceived in a test-tube. Had her first back in April. A daughter.'

Zieminski continued reading. 'Does anything strike you as odd about this list?' he asked, as soon as he had finished.

'*Odd*?' Mancini frowned. 'How do you mean, odd?'

'Well, for a start, they're all rich. Okay, so I know *all* of Snaith's patients are rich. But some reject.' Zieminski slapped the paper with the back of his hand. 'All of the people on this list are *rich* rich, and apparently none of them have rejected. Doesn't that strike you as *odd*?'

'What's odd about it? Like the man says, you gets what you pay for . . .'

Zieminski handed back the list. 'That was going to be my next question,' he said, putting away his glasses. 'How much does one of Snaith's transplants set you back? A new heart, for example . . .'

26

'I'm not really sure. I only know that Spiegel's didn't come cheap.'

'Fifty thousand dollars?' Zieminsky prompted.

Mancini laughed. 'You've gotta be *joking*!'

'A hundred thousand, then?'

'Closer to a million.'

'A *million*?' Zieminski stared at him in astonishment. 'A million dollars for a *heart transplant*?'

Suddenly looking very troubled, Zieminski got up and began wandering around the room, jingling the loose change in his trouser pockets. 'I don't get it,' he said at last. 'I just don't get it. What did Spiegel think he was getting for his million bucks? Snaith has to get his organs the same way as any other surgeon – through the Transplantation Service.'

Mancini started to say something, but Zieminski stopped him. 'Look, let's go through this thing in sequence,' he said, picking up the eight-ball from Mancini's blue-topped pool table. 'What happens is this: a physician finds himself with a patient suffering from irreversible brain damage. Okay? The patient's heart's still beating, but according to all currently accepted standards of what is meant by death, he's dead. So, the physician calls the Transplantation Service and says he has a beating-heart cadaver on offer. The Transplantation Service checks the guy's blood group and tissue type against the data they carry on all potential recipients, and the recipient with the closest match and the highest priority rating gets the heart.

'Now, let's assume Snaith's prepared to put your name on the transplantation list. You're forty-eight, which, let's face it, isn't exactly *young*, and your heart's not all that bad. So, without a donor turns up whose blood group and tissue type matches yours exactly – and God alone knows what the odds are against *that* happening – the donor heart'll go to a younger, sicker patient than you.

'Or at least that's what *should* happen,' he added, suddenly sending the eight-ball hurtling across the pool table. 'Without the guys who run the Transplantation Service are on the take from Snaith!'

'Just now you were coming on about him like he was Jesus

27

Christ Almighty,' Mancini grumbled. 'Now you're saying he's Nick the Greek.'

'Okay, okay!' said Zieminski. Another idea was taking shape in his mind. 'Just hold it for a minute . . .' He began scratching the side of his face. 'I suppose it's *just* possible that he might be buying organs—'

'Buying them?' Mancini looked worried. 'You mean, like from the goddamned *morgue*?'

'Not from the morgue – from people. From living people. It won't be the first time it's happened. An Italian sold one of his testicles for transplantation back in the '30s, and I personally know of at least one Saudi Arabian sheik who bought himself a kidney. Bought it from one of his herdsmen.

'I guess if you look long enough and hard enough, you'd find someone of the correct blood group and tissue type who'd be prepared to sell you one of their kidneys if the money's right, or even their Fallopian tubes. After all, you can get by perfectly well with just one kidney, and if you don't want children, who needs Fallopian tubes . . .'

Mancini nodded. 'Sounds like a good theory to me,' he said, glancing at his wristwatch. 'Abe, it's getting late, and I've—'

'It's a lousy theory,' said Zieminski flatly. 'Particularly when it comes to the heart. What kind of a nut is going to sell you his *heart*?'

'Okay, so it's a lousy theory!' Mancini flung his cigar into the fireplace, got up and started for the door. 'Frankly, I don't give a fuck! How Snaith gets his hearts is his problem. Mine is that I want one, and yours—' he paused to jab a finger at Zieminski '—yours is to fix that I get it!'

4

Ten minutes after it had first broken through the towering
banks of black cumulus cloud above Miami International Airport, Mancini's gold DC7 rolled to a standstill on the parking
ramp. To enable him to travel in the ultimate comfort, two
million dollars had been spent on refurbishing the interior
alone. There was a lounge hung with early American primitive
paintings, a galley, two bedrooms with adjoining bathrooms,
and – a recent innovation – a hospital compartment equipped
with sophisticated telemetry so that, if necessary, his heart
could be monitored by his cardiologist via satellite.

As flight-line personnel darted forward to plug the ground
power unit into the aircraft's underbelly, a set of airstairs was
manoeuvred into position alongside a forward passenger door.
The door was thrown open by a member of the cabin crew,
and, after two bodyguards had reassured themselves that the
area was secure, Mancini and his radiantly beautiful young
wife appeared.

As they did so, TV camera crews and a crowd of press photographers and reporters burst through a cordon of sullen-look-
ing policemen, raced past Zieminski and on to the ramp, where
they began jostling one another for position at the foot of the
airstairs.

Flashlights began popping, and Mrs Mancini – as if respond-
ing to a Pavlovian conditioned reflex – tossed back her long,
fashionably untidy ash-blonde hair and went straight into her
movie-actress-arriving-at-a-première routine.

Accompanied by his bodyguards, Mancini started down the
airstairs towards the thicket of microphones that were being
held out to him. What was he doing in Miami? Where would
he be staying? Why was he supporting the Firearms Control
Bill?

Mancini held up his hands for silence. 'Why have I come to
Miami? For a couple of days' peace and quiet.' The reporters
began scribbling furiously. 'Which is why,' he added, amid a

ripple of appreciative laughter, 'I shan't be answering your second question!

'Why am I supporting the Firearms Control Bill?' His voice took on a more serious tone. 'Well, as you boys know, it's not that I'm against guns as such. However, it's high time that something was done to keep 'em out of the hands of psychopaths and criminals, and maybe this Bill will help some . . .'

'But you've always argued that tougher law enforcement was the way to do that,' said one of the TV reporters, 'not more restrictive gun-control legislation.' He thrust his microphone forward for Mancini's comment.

'I don't consider that this Bill *is* particularly restrictive. Hunters and members of properly run sporting clubs – in fact anyone of good character and with a legitimate need for a gun – will still be allowed a gun.

'Let's not confuse *restrictive* with *effective*,' he added, beginning to look around for Zieminski. 'The only way the proposed legislation is going to be effective *is* with tougher law enforcement.'

Another reporter began speaking. 'A spokesman for the National Rifle Association has described your about-face on the issue of firearms control as—'

'It's not an about-face!' snapped Mancini.

'About-face was his word, not mine. According to him it's the quote biggest sellout since Judas Iscariot unquote. What do you have to say to that?'

'Only that if anyone's likely to be sold out on this issue, it's the American people. It's the American people who've been demanding more effective gun control, and it's the American people who'll suffer if they don't *get* more effective gun control.

'Let's not forget that civilian casualties from gunfire this century exceed our military casualties in every war from the American Revolution to Vietnam!'

Having at last spotted Zieminski, Mancini began edging his way through the microphones.

'You've been one of the President's most outspoken critics,' said a reporter wearing a lapel button issued by the Informed Citizens' Campaign to Disarm America. 'Does your support for the Bill mean you've revised your opinion of the man?'

Now on the tarmac, Mancini turned and grabbed hold of his wife's elbow. 'Let's get one thing straight,' he said, moving forward against the press of bodies. 'I consider his to have been the most woefully inept Administration since Eisenhower's. This Bill's the first thing he's come up with in seven years that makes any kind of sense. Seven *years*!'

There was a rumble of thunder, and the first drops of rain – fat as bumble-bees – began to fall out of the darkening sky.

'But Mr Mancini—'

'Sorry boys, but that's it!' he said, bundling his wife and then Zieminski into the first of the waiting limousines.

The chauffeur slammed the door after Mancini, and, with his head ducked against the now torrential rain, ran around the front and jumped in.

'C'mon, let's go!' yelled a police officer, thumping the roof with the flat of his hand. '*Move* it!'

Almost too late, Tony Giordano (Chief of Security for the Eldorado Corporation) leapt in beside Mrs Mancini and the limousine accelerated away.

'In case any of those bums try to follow us,' he said, twisting around to look through the rear window, 'I've arranged to switch cars at Moore Park. Instead of going across the Julia Tuttle, we'll head north and get on to the Beach via the 79th Street Causeway.' After pausing to look at his watch, he added: 'Without the traffic gets snarled up by the weather, we should have time to drop Mrs Mancini off at the Fountainebleau before going to the Snaith Clinic.'

'Fine.' Mancini took a bottle of nitro-glycerine tablets from his pocket and popped one in his mouth. 'Now, what's security like at Snaith's clinics?' Ever since an attempt had been made to kidnap him two years earlier, he had been very security conscious.

'It's good,' replied Giordano. 'Very good. In fact the one he has in the Bahamas was set up specially for patients like yourself. Patients at risk from kidnappers, terrorists, hit-men . . . Right now he's got a couple of sheiks hospitalized there, a West German industrialist, and a Grand Jury witness with a perforated ulcer that the Department of Justice is very anxious doesn't get blown away!'

'And what about getting there? How are people supposed to get to see me on the island?'

'No problem. Snaith runs a regular helicopter shuttle from Watson Park.

'Oh – and another thing,' Giordano added, 'I've arranged to have a scrambler telephone installed in your suite, a telex and transaction tickers. So, if you decide to go ahead with the operation, it should be a regular home from home!'

Mancini frowned. 'How do you mean, *if* I decide to go ahead with the operation?' He turned to Zieminski, who was perched on one of the jump-seats, trying to dry his hair with a handkerchief. 'It *is* all fixed, isn't't?'

'Fixed?' Zieminski hated riding on jump-seats as much as he hated crowds and getting wet. 'The only thing that's *fixed* is that Snaith's agreed to see you,' he replied irritably.

Mancini stared uncomprehendingly at the others. 'You're kidding,' he said, turning back to Zieminski. 'You mean you've been here for forty-eight hours and all you've fixed is for me to *see* him?'

'Well, it hasn't been easy . . .'

'Okay, so it hasn't been easy,' said Mancini, determined to keep his cool. 'But you've found out how it is he's able to guarantee a heart that won't be rejected?'

Zieminski shook his head. 'No one's even mentioned such a guarantee, much less given one.' His tone hardened. 'Frank, I know you're going to Snaith because you think he's able to bend the rules in some way; but listen, there's not a scrap of evidence to support that belief. Not a scrap. As far as I can see, he's playing it strictly by the book.'

'But what about the *money*?' Mancini demanded. 'If he's playing it by the goddamned book, what's the money supposed to buy? Or haven't you talked to him about that either?'

'I haven't talked to *Snaith* about money—'

'But you've talked to someone?'

'I talked to a guy called Quintrell. Quintrell's some sort of an administrative assistant—'

'*Quintrell*?' Mancini turned to Giordano. 'What do we know about him?'

Giordano consulted his notebook. 'Quintrell. Yes, here we

are. He was an administrator at the Denton Cooley at the same time as Snaith, and left with him to handle the organization of his research project. When they lowered the boom on that, he helped him set up down here. In fact he's Snaith's senior administrator.'

'*Senior* administrator, then.' Zieminski sighed. 'Anyway, Quintrell said that you'd be billed a hundred and fifty thousand dollars, give or take a couple of grand either way.'

Mancini exchanged expressions of alarm with his wife, who, until then, had been preoccupied with trying to repair the damage done to her make-up by the rain. '*How* much?' he asked Zieminski.

'One hundred and fifty thousand dollars. But hold your horses! This guy Quintrell *then* starts telling me about something called the Abaco Research Foundation that Snaith's supposed to have set up to study improved methods of organ transplantation—'

'Christ, Abe,' said Mancini, letting out his breath, 'you had me worried there for a minute. Okay, so I'm supposed to make a donation to this Foundation of Snaith's. How much and when?'

'You weren't *asked* to. Let me make that quite clear. Nobody *asked* you to donate a cent. He just sort of – sort of told me about it in passing.'

'All right, but he didn't say no when you offered it, did he?'

'No, he didn't . . .'

'So, what *happened*?' asked Mancini, with mounting impatience. 'Getting answers out of you is worse than drawing teeth!'

'I said that improving transplantation techniques was a subject close to your heart—'

'Very funny!' said Mancini, but he didn't laugh.

'—and that I thought you'd be good for a quarter of a million dollars. "*Three*-quarters of a million dollars!" said Quintrell, as if he hadn't heard me. "That's really most generous!"'

'Well, there you go!' said Mancini, looking pleased with himself. 'We're off and running!'

Zieminski turned to look out of the window. The clouds had parted to let the sun through, and there was the beginning of a rainbow over Miami Springs. 'But what's three-quarters of a million bucks above the line supposed to buy?' he asked, as if talking to himself. 'That's what I can't figure out. Maybe it doesn't buy anything . . . Maybe the fact that he hasn't had one of his *rich* rich patients reject – maybe that's just chance . . .'

'And maybe the Pope sniffs coke!' said Mancini. 'Anyway, what about Snaith? Tell me about him.'

'He was born in London,' Zieminski began, 'educated at Harrow and—'

'I *know* all that. I mean like what sort of a *guy* is he?'

'He's very—' Zieminski shrugged. 'I guess he's very English.'

'Very English?' Giordano began chuckling.

'Okay, so he's cold,' said Zieminski, defensively. 'Polite but cold . . .'

'Boy, oh boy! I'm tellin' you, that sonuvabitch is *so* cold I damn near froze to death just being in the same room with him!'

Mancini's eyes flicked from one man to the other. 'But he doesn't bear me a grudge, does he?' he asked. 'I mean, that's not what it's all about, is it?'

'A guy like Snaith wouldn't show it even if he did,' replied Zieminski.

'You mean you don't know?' said Mancini indignantly. 'Christ, Abe, I don't want the motherfucker leaving a pair of artery forceps inside me!'

'And have you hit him with a malpractice suit?' Zieminski waved away the suggestion disdainfully.

Mancini slumped back against the car seat. 'Abe, you've really screwed up on this deal, haven't you?' he said in a pained, exhausted voice. 'You've really let this guy run rings around you. Well, he may have run rings around you, but there's no way he's going to run rings around me! No *way*! For a million bucks, if I want him to lay an egg, boy will he strain!'

5

'Dr Snaith,' said the nurse, ushering Mancini into a room which looked like the library of an exclusive London men's club, 'Mr Mancini for you.'

Snaith, who was sitting writing at a desk in the middle of the room, glanced at him over the top of a pair of gold half-frame spectacles. 'Ah yes, of course,' he said, in a rich, well-modulated English voice. 'Do please come in.'

The nurse withdrew, closing the door quietly behind her, and Snaith continued writing for a moment more. Then, as a long-case clock began chiming the hour, he rose, and, with a thin smile, came around and shook hands with Mancini.

Although in his middle sixties, he had the bearing of a much younger man. He was tall and upright, and he moved in a brisk, purposeful manner. He had a lean, patrician face, deeply set eyes and black bushy eyebrows that contrasted oddly with his carefully brushed silver hair. In the buttonhole of his grey suit was a tiny rosebud which exactly matched the pink of his shirt, and he was wearing an Old Harrovian tie and a pearl tie-pin. His manner was courteous but reserved, almost to the point of aloofness.

'Please,' he said, indicating that Mancini was to sit opposite him in one of the leather-covered club chairs that were standing either side of an Adam fireplace. 'Now, what seems to be the matter?'

'What seems to be the *matter*?' growled Mancini, irritated to have been kept waiting even for a moment. 'I thought Zieminski had already been over my case with you?'

'And so he has. Most thoroughly, if I may say so. Nevertheless, I would like to hear it from you, if you'd be so kind. It is, after all, as important to know what sort of a man has a disease as it is to know what sort of a disease a man has.'

Mancini shrugged. 'What's there to tell? My heart's got too many miles on the clock and I want to trade it in for a new model.'

'I see,' said Snaith, non-committally. He took off his spec-

35

tacles and began polishing them with a white handkerchief he kept tucked up his sleeve. There was a moment's silence, broken only by the ticking of the long-case clock in the corner, and then he said: 'I take it you know that Dr Zieminski isn't in favour of your having a transplant? He feels that there isn't sufficient wrong with your heart to justify the risks attached to such an operation.'

'Zieminski's an old woman.'

'Oh, come, come,' said Snaith, a hint of reproach in his voice. 'By the way, may I presume to ask why it is you've come to me?'

'Because I've been told that if the money's right, you can fix me up with a heart that won't be rejected,' replied Mancini, determined to do what Zieminski had failed to do – cut through the crap, and quick.

Snaith raised his eyebrows quizzically. 'Have you, indeed?' he said, drawing out the words like warm toffee. 'How very interesting.'

'Well, can't you?'

'There is only one thing certain, namely that we can have nothing certain,' Snaith replied, 'and therefore it is not certain that we can have nothing certain.' He smiled cryptically. 'Samuel Butler.'

'What kind of an answer is that?'

'The best you're going to get, I'm afraid.'

Mancini nodded. 'Okay, if that's the way you want to play it,' he said, taking a diary out of the pocket of his black leather trucker's jacket. 'So, we've agreed a price; now can we agree a delivery date?'

Snaith cleared his throat. 'I'm afraid it isn't quite as easy as that,' he explained stiffly. 'First we'll have to carry out tests to establish whether or not—'

'Tests?' Mancini felt himself becoming angry. 'What tests? Christ, I was almost tested to destruction in Houston!'

'Nevertheless, there will have to be tests. Putting a new heart into a body which may already have begun to adapt itself to a damaged one would be rather like putting a Rolls Royce engine into a Volkswagen, if I, too, may be permitted to use a motoring analogy. And as well as *physio*logical tests, there'll have to be psychological tests.'

'*Psychological* tests?' Mancini's anger mounted. 'There's no way you're going to get me to take any psychological tests! No way!'

Unperturbed by Mancini's outburst, Snaith said: 'No responsible surgeon would carry out a heart transplant without first reassuring himself that his patient was capable of withstanding the psychological as well as the physiological trauma of such an operation.' He crossed one leg over another. 'After all,' he added, removing a piece of lint from the knee of his trousers, 'the heart, perhaps more than any other organ of the human body, is the most richly endowed with mystical associations.'

'As far as I'm concerned it's just a fuckin' pump!'

'Fine!' Snaith permitted himself a flicker of a smile. 'In that case you should have no difficulty with the psychological tests!'

Mancini held up his hands. 'All right!' he said, as if Snaith was the one who needed to be calmed. 'If you want to go through all this bullshit for the sake of appearances, well – all right. But let's get one thing straight – I don't want it holding up the parade. Okay?'

'If and when it is agreed that a transplant is indicated—'

'If and when?' Mancini's anger finally boiled over. 'A million bucks for a goddamned heart transplant and you're talking about if and when?'

'*Two* million dollars, Mr Mancini,' said Snaith icily. 'The price has just gone up to two million dollars.'

6

Snaith laid aside his copy of the *New England Journal of Medicine* and turned to look down through the plexiglass dome of the Bell 47-J helicopter that had brought him on the thirty-minute journey from Miami.

Since first reading *Treasure Island* as a boy, islands had fascinated him, and none more than those below him – the summits of a submerged mountain range known as the Bahamas.

Stretching some 750 miles southeastwards from a point fifty miles off the coast of Florida and bisected by the Tropic of Cancer, the Bahamas have long been associated with buccaneering activities. Discovered by Columbus on October 12th, 1492, the islands have served as a pirate stronghold, a depot for ships running guns and ammunition through the blockade imposed against the Confederate States by the Union Government, an entrepôt for bootleggers, and the headquarters of a Mafia-controlled gambling empire.

The island which Snaith owned lay to the north of Abaco. Surrounded by crystal-clear, turquoise water, it rose from a shore of pink coral sand to a low ridge. Strung out along the ridge were the island's principal buildings: the clinic itself – a dazzlingly white, three-storey neo-Colonial structure with pillared portico, louvred windows and balconies; a flat-roofed, concrete and glass laboratory; and a cluster of gaily painted staff bungalows.

With the help of a solar-powered desalination plant and 10,000 tons of humus shipped in to supplement the island's meagre topsoil, landscape designers and an army of gardeners had made a little Eden of the surrounding grounds. There were magnificent stands of cedar, mahogany and casuarina pine, and gardens ablaze with over a hundred varieties of flowering shrub. There were pools, fountains and cascades; grottoes and grape arbours. And in front of the clinic there was an enormous, impeccable rolled lawn on which peacocks strutted.

Jutting out into the channel which separated the island from the mainland was a marina with dockage for twenty boats.

At 1,200 feet, the pilot – having identified himself and received landing clearance – began to take the helicopter down towards the island. As they settled on to the shimmering concrete pad, a battery-operated field car driven by an armed guard pulled away from beside the waiting fire tender and stopped just short of the helicopter's rotating blades. Snaith stepped out into the 90 degrees heat. It was exactly ten minutes before noon – time enough for him to change out of his flame-resistant flight-suit into the black coat and striped trousers he would wear until returning later that afternoon.

Snaith had not been unduly dismayed when, five years earlier, he had suddenly found himself accused of unwarranted interference with the life processes. After all, the history of science and medicine was crowded with men and women who, like himself, had been vilified for daring to swim against the tide of public opinion. Nor had he, even for a moment, considered abandoning his research. It was too important. However, there had been one serious problem: in order to continue with his work, he would need a huge infrastructure of apparatus and support staff. And that would cost money – more money than he could ever hope to earn legitimately.

But then he had remembered how surprised he'd been, on first arriving in the United States, to discover that there were twice as many surgical operations per head of population being performed there each year than in Britain. Only when he had heard an American colleague use the term 'remunerectomy' had the truth dawned on him: unscrupulous surgeons were making a practice of removing perfectly healthy organs from patients. The situation had been summed up by a specialist in community health: 'What we have going on over here,' he told Snaith, 'is a medical version of Parkinson's Law – patient admissions for surgery expand to fill beds, operating suites and surgeons' time!'

Although he had been deeply shocked, a decade later Snaith was to decide that the circumstances were now such as to justify *him* taking a more buccaneering approach to medicine.

It had not taken him long to come up with the broad outline of an idea. Among the tens of thousands of patients throughout the world who were waiting for a transplant, there were, he knew, many able and willing to pay a king's ransom to get to the head of a transplantation list. Finding the patients would not be a problem – Snaith's fame as a transplanter was already world-wide. The trick would be to find a way of introducing into the system donors whose blood group and tissue type matched that of his patient so perfectly that the people running the Transplantation Service would rarely, if ever, have any option other than to assign the donor to Snaith.

The fact that he would have to make himself a party to murder in order to implement such a scheme caused him few qualms. Like many doctors, he had become, if not exactly desensitized to death, at least familiar with it. Furthermore, he had never been a proponent of the life-at-any-cost ethic; he believed that it was not life that mattered, but quality of life. All of us have to die sooner or later. So what if a few – chosen with the impartiality of fate itself – died sooner rather than later? Measured against the hundreds of thousands who would one day be restored to active life as a result of his work, it was a small price to pay – only a fraction of that which society was prepared to pay each year in order to enjoy the doubtful benefits of the automobile, or even the immunization programme.

He had even fewer qualms about not giving society any choice in the matter. Had it not already demonstrated its inability to view the issues objectively? And anyway, governments were for ever taking life-and-death decisions on behalf of society. Who, for example, had ever heard of a government taking a referendum before declaring war?

It was then that a former patient – an arms dealer who had helped finance and organize a Unilateral Declaration of Independence on behalf of the 7,000 inhabitants of Abaco – had told him that one of the small islands to the north of Marsh Harbour would be coming up for sale.

Such an island suited Snaith's purposes admirably (some American doctors had already set up in the Bahamas in order to practise medical techniques illegal in the United States), and he had immediately asked for and been given an option.

The key to the implementation of his plan, however, was to elude him for several weeks. There was no question of abducting at random the people destined to become donors – the odds against any of them turning out to be of the required blood group and tissue type were vanishingly small.

The answer had come while revisiting England to attend an International Histocompatibility Workshop. There, Snaith had bumped into Guy Ward-Roper, a man who had been on the same staircase as himself at Cambridge. Ward-Roper was Director of Information Services for the Institute of Preventive Medicine, and over dinner that evening they had begun arguing about the value of multiphasic health screening, with Snaith making the case that such screenings did little except turn healthy people into patients without significantly increasing their life-expectancy.

'Oh, come now!' Ward-Roper had said indignantly. 'That might have been true once, but things have changed a lot recently. Look, since we introduced tissue-typing into our repertoire—'

'*Tissue-typing*?' Snaith had felt a sudden prickle of excitement at the back of his neck. 'Good God!'

'Don't look so surprised! You know as well as I do that pernicious anaemia, for example, has been associated with HLA B12 and B18; ankylosing spondylitis with—'

'Quite so,' Snaith had said, no longer interested in trying to score debating points. 'But do you mean to say you're HLA-typing *all* your patients?'

Ward-Roper had nodded. 'We're the first multiphasic screening unit in the world to do so,' he'd replied proudly. 'As a matter of fact, there's going to be a big article about it in the *BMJ* next month.

'Of course, dear boy, I know it's still too early to be absolutely *certain* about the correlation between—'

'And how many people did you say you screen in a year?' Snaith had asked impatiently.

'In London, about twenty thousand. But we also have units in West Germany, France, Italy, Sweden and Holland, so I suppose we're talking about something in the region of a million a year.

'And that's only the beginning; soon, we expect to be opening units in the States, Canada and Aussieland.'

Aware that he had stumbled on to what might well be the key to his plan, Snaith had worked hard to conceal his excitement.

'Well, well, well! How absolutely fascinating! Tell me, how long do you keep their records?'

'Indefinitely.'

'Really?'

'Oh, yes. That's most important,' Ward-Roper had explained. 'A baseline reading facilitates the interpretation of later readings . . .'

'And these records are – what? – kept on a computer, presumably?'

'But of course, dear boy,' Ward-Roper had replied, busying himself with the ritual of selecting a cigar. 'With a throughput of a million patients a year, computer storage of case notes is the only thing that makes sense.'

Snaith had finally found what he had been looking for: a huge, ever-expanding repository of information about potential donors.

The next problem had been to find a way of persuading Ward-Roper to join him in his enterprise. Money would clearly not be a sufficiently strong inducement. As Director of Information Services, Snaith guessed he would be earning between £15,000 and £20,000 a year. And anyway, Ward-Roper's titled wife was known to be immensely rich in her own right.

However, he knew that Ward-Roper had political ambitions. He also knew that, as an undergraduate, Ward-Roper had been a practising homosexual, and that in Britain homosexuality and politics did not mix (only a few years earlier, a privy councillor had been obliged to resign as leader of his party following an allegation that he, too, had once had a homosexual relationship).

That being the case, might not Ward-Roper be prepared to go to almost any length to keep his sexual proclivities a secret, particularly if he was still giving vent to them?

The following day, Snaith had commissioned a private detective agency to carry out an investigation into Ward-Roper's background and life-style (in order to make his rationale for such an inquiry more convincing, he'd also had two other computer experts vetted at the same time).

What the agency had come up with had exceeded Snaith's wildest expectations; not only was Ward-Roper still a practising homosexual, many of his sexual partners were convicted criminals.

At his next meeting with Ward-Roper, Snaith had opened in what he regarded as a gentlemanly fashion. What he wanted, he had explained, was access to the Institute's patient record file. 'That's all you'll have to provide and all you'll need to know,' he had told him. 'In return you will receive an equivalent of £10,000 per annum in any currency you choose to nominate, made payable to a numbered bank account in Zurich.'

Ward-Roper had refused to consider the proposition, and Snaith had had to play his trump card.

At first it had looked as if even the threat of blackmail was not going to work, and Ward-Roper had stormed out of Snaith's hotel room threatening to go to the police.

But the following day he had returned. 'Providing you can assure me that – although improperly obtained – the information will not be improperly used, I'll do what you want,' he'd said. 'But I'll rot in hell before I take a penny-piece for it.'

The following morning Snaith had returned to Miami and taken up the option to buy the island. With what he regarded as a pleasingly ironical touch, he renamed it Hippocrates Cay and set about the task of recruiting the remainder of his staff.

Having made his rounds and dealt with a number of clinical and administrative problems which had arisen since his visit the previous day, Snaith made his way across from the hospital to the laboratory.

The building – a rectangular framed structure of raw concrete in-filled with brick and raised above the ground on two rows of columns – looked no more forbidding than any other designed in the style known as New Brutalism. At least, not until one realized that although it clearly had two floors, only the first had windows, and even they were made from one-way mirror glass – allowing those inside to see out, but not those outside to see in. Access was by way of a flight of steps leading to a steel door flanked by a pair of closed-circuit television cameras. Inscribed on the lintel was the motto of the Abaco Research Foundation: *Ne cede malis sed contra audentior ito* – Do not yield to misfortunes, on the contrary, go more boldly to meet them.

Snaith climbed the steps and announced himself on the entryphone. There was a moment's delay while the television cameras looked him over, and then the door slid silently to one side and he entered a neat, business-like foyer. After giving a curt nod to the two armed guards who were keeping watch on a bank of television monitors, he climbed a flight of stairs, walked along a corridor also covered by a television camera, and unlocked the door to his office.

Unlike the consulting room in his Miami Beach clinic, the room was small and had been furnished without ostentation. Painted white throughout, it contained a desk, a couple of chairs and a settee, filing cabinets and a computer terminal like those used by airlines for flight reservations. Connected to the terminal was a telephone and an electronic interpreter known as an acoustic modem.

Snaith crossed to the terminal, picked up the telephone and dialled a number that gave him direct access to the computer at the Institute of Preventive Medicine, then clamped the handset into the modem pads.

The previous week he had used this same terminal to instruct the computer to begin a search for patients of the same blood group and tissue type as Mancini. During an average 24-hour day, the computer file was accessed many thousands of times by legitimate users, and by an ingenious piece of sub-programming Ward-Roper had instructed it – on a command from Snaith – to search neighbouring records each time it made a legitimate access. If, during these sly glances, it discovered a patient whose blood group and tissue type matched those of Snaith's patient, the computer accessed the complete medical profile, directed a duplicate to a private record that Ward-Roper had nominated and sealed it with a lockword. A further routine erased any evidence of the illegal search. It was as if a wagon had been shunted off the computing mainline into Ward-Roper's siding, and the points changed.

The beauty of the system was that the extra computer traffic generated was negligible; by the end of a week it was possible to survey sometimes as much as 80 per cent of the file yet leave no overt trace. Anything other than such a carefully staggered search would have led to a suspiciously high recording of accesses per programme in the data logs – the sort of gross irregularities that would have been immediately apparent to Ward-Roper's staff and the performance-measurement consultants who regularly tuned the computer.

Snaith sat down and began tapping out a 12-character password on the terminal keyboard. Use of the password – equivalent to a combination lock on a safe, and known only to himself and Ward-Roper – both identified Snaith as an authorized user and ensured that the exchange that was about to take place was secure from accidental recall by other users of the computer. As a protection against wire-tapping, a device which converted clear-text messages to cipher-text had been built into the modem.

As soon as he had finished typing the password, Snaith entered it into the computer by pressing the carriage return. Immediately, a pin-point of green light began racing to and fro across the screen, leaving in its wake the words:

```
SHORT FORM OF DIALOG FOR DONOR-RECIPIENT MATCH
ANSWER ALL YES OR NO QUESTIONS WITH y OR n
YOU HAVE ENTERED THIS ABO TYPE:
AB
CORRECT?
```

The computer waited until Snaith had typed the letter y, the short form for *yes.*

```
YOU HAVE ENTERED THESE ANTIGENS:
HLA-A SERIES: A1A2
HLA-B SERIES: B8B12
HLA-C SERIES: C4CX
HLA-D SERIES: D3D7
CORRECT?
```

Again, Snaith typed y.

HOW MANY DO YOU WANT PRINTED? TYPE A NUMBER OR 'ALL' OR
'NONE'

Snaith typed ALL, and the computer replied:

THE FOLLOWING DONOR(S) MATCH 8 RECIPIENT ANTIGENS:

REG NO	A G	S X	R C	ABO	HLA-A	HLA-B	HLA-C	HLA-D
00201279	51	M	CAUC	AB	A1A2	B8B12	C4CX	D3D7

DO YOU WANT FULL PATIENT PROFILE? TYPE REGISTERED
NUMBER OR 'ALL' OR 'NONE'

With a long-suffering sigh Snaith typed ALL. Although he understood why the computer had been programmed to play back
data entered into it from distant terminals (it was as a check
against the transmission of incomplete data caused by static
interruption on the telephone line), the programme requiring
him to answer what he regarded as manifestly irrelevant questions irritated him greatly.

Snaith ran his eye down the medical profile displayed on the
screen. At fifty-one, patient No. 00201279 was a shade too old,
and he was showing signs of valvular trouble.

There was nothing for it but to call up the list of patients
with 7-way matches. Clearly, he would have preferred a donor
with a full-house match. But the odds were still overwhelming
against there being anyone else on the transplantation list with
even a 7-way match, so, providing the mismatched antigens
were on the relatively unimportant A or C loci, there was unlikely to be a problem. D-locus mismatches, however, he was
careful to avoid; in transplantation they have a disastrous
effect.

Once again the computer blinked up the required data:

THE FOLLOWING DONOR(S) MATCH 7 RECIPIENT ANTIGENS:

REG NO	A G	S X	R C	ABO	HLA-A	HLA-B	HLA-C	HLA-D
01010239	31	M	CAUC	AB	A1A2	B8B12	C4CX	D4D7
02261493	32	M	CAUC	AB	A1A2	B8B12	C3CX	D3D7
03114572	22	F	CAUC	AB	A1A2	B8B12	C4C5	D3D7

DO YOU WANT FULL PATIENT PROFILE? TYPE REGISTERED
NUMBER OR 'ALL' OR 'NONE'

Snaith hesitated. An idea had begun to take shape in his mind. What would happen if he were to give Mancini – the personification of everything he detested – the heart of the man with signs of valvular trouble? Driving himself as he did, it was almost inevitable that within a couple of years he would be in need of further surgery. With luck, he might even drop dead. Moreover, since the responsibility for offering the man as a donor rested with the referring physician and the Transplantation Service, there was absolutely no risk of his being held accountable.

It was an interesting idea; unscientific, but interesting. *Very* interesting.

But then Snaith felt his initial flush of excitement beginning to drain away. The trouble with revenge, he reflected, is that it is essentially irrational, and he was someone who prided himself on being wholly rational. If, by such an act of revenge, he could have undone the wrong done to him by Mancini, he would not have hesitated. But that would not be the case. On the contrary, as Francis Bacon had said: 'A man that studieth revenge keeps his own wounds green.'

With a twinge of regret, Snaith redirected his attention to the computer terminal. Displayed on the screen was the question: DO YOU WANT PROMPTING?

NO I DO NOT, he typed, with more force than was necessary.

PLEASE OBSERVE STANDARD DIALOG, the computer replied. ANSWER ALL YES OR NO QUESTIONS WITH y OR n. DO YOU WANT PROMPTING?

Snaith hit the n key, and then began typing the last two patient registration numbers (the first he ignored – with a D-locus mismatch, the man was of no use to him).

Once again the pin-point of light began racing to and fro across the screen, displaying the profiles for which he had asked. Apart from the fact that one was of a man and the other a woman, there was little to choose between them. True, the woman was slightly anaemic, but otherwise both appeared to be in exceptionally good health.

In such a situation, Snaith would normally have selected a donor of the same sex as the recipient. However, somewhere deep inside him the yearning for revenge was still very much alive.

The psychological tests which had been carried out on Mancini had shown his aggressive, overbearing manner to be a defence against profound self-doubts about his masculinity. Supposing, then, that he was to be given the *woman*'s heart? Although functionally it would serve him equally as well as the man's (perhaps even better, since she was ten years younger), might it not make him feel in some way emasculated? Of one thing he was certain: Mancini would not want it known that beneath his heavily muscled, hairy chest lay the heart of a mere woman. In which case he could use the threat of revelation as a bridle with which to curb him, were it ever again to become necessary.

Pleased with himself for having found a meaningful reason for gratifying his urge to hurt Mancini, Snaith tapped out the password that gave him access to the names and addresses of patients, followed by the young woman's registration number. Immediately, the computer replied:

```
PATIENT NO 03114572
SURNAME: TENNANT
FORENAME(S): CLAIR ANN
ADDRESS: 62 TITE STREET, LONDON, S.W.3, BRITAIN.
```

7

Hiring a small car had seemed like a good idea at the time; it would be easy to park, and inconspicuous. However, having spent the best part of four hours cooped up inside it, Paul Ginzel was having second thoughts; second thoughts not only about the wisdom of a tall, massively built man hiring a small car, but also about whether Clair Tennant would be coming home that night.

And then, just as he was about to get out and stretch his cramped legs, he caught sight of her in the rear-view mirror.

'Okay, we're in business,' he announced, stubbing out his cigarette.

The middle-aged, rather horsy-looking woman sitting next to him opened her eyes, blinked, and after glancing at her gold Cartier wristwatch, twisted around to look through the rear window. For the past half-hour she had been sitting with her hands folded in her lap, meditating. Now she felt rested and relaxed, and fully capable of the task which lay ahead.

Although like Ginzel, Martha Pierce worked as a body-snatcher for Snaith (they were known to the other members of his organization as 'Burke and Hare'), in her Hermès head-scarf, navy blazer and grey, pleated skirt she could have passed for any one of a multitude of women to be found every after-noon in Harrods. Formerly Snaith's scrub nurse at the Denton Cooley Memorial Hospital, she had returned to her home-town of Boston to open a geriatric clinic with money left to her by her husband (a former patient, thirty years her senior). However, although she had been an excellent nurse, she was a poor businesswoman, and had soon found herself in financial difficulties. And then, while negotiating her third mortgage, her clinic had burned to the ground. Charged with manslaugh-ter, arson and conspiracy to defraud an insurance company, she had called Snaith and asked him if he would stand bail for her. Not only had he agreed, but at his own expense had hired the best trial lawyers in Massachusetts to defend her, as well as a team of social scientists, market researchers and body-language specialists to help them select a jury favourable to the defence.

Not surprisingly, Pierce had been acquitted on all three charges. It was then that Snaith had offered her her present job, a job which – obligated as she was – she felt she had no option but to accept.

'Well, what do you think?' she asked Ginzel, as Clair, now at the front door, began searching for her latchkey in the big canvas bag she was carrying. She spoke softly, and with just a trace of a Bostonian accent.

'What do I think about what?'

'About my going in . . . You don't think it's too late?'

Ginzel looked at his watch. 'Nine o'clock isn't all that late. And anyway, how do we know she won't be later tomorrow, or have someone with her?' He shrugged. 'While the cat's away . . .'

'I guess so.' Pierce reached behind her for her crocodile-skin handbag and took out a powder compact and lipstick. 'Okay, so let's get it over with.'

Leaving her to freshen up, he strolled down the road to a telephone box and dialled Clair's number.

As soon as she answered, he pressed a coin into the slot and said: 'Can I speak to Mr Vernon, please?'

'Mr Vernon? I think you must have the wrong number. This is three five two, four five—'

'I'm sorry! I wanted *four* five two . . .'

Ginzel waited until he heard her ring off, then took a lump of Plasticine out of his pocket and rammed it beneath the cradle before replacing the handset. Until he removed the Plasticine, anyone ringing Clair's number would get a line engaged signal; it was a simple but effective way of ensuring that once inside the flat, Pierce would not be disturbed.

After hanging an Out of Order notice over the phone, he returned to the car.

'Have you got everything?' he asked, nodding at Pierce's handbag.

'I've got it, but I don't think I'll be needing it,' she replied, examining her large, slightly protruberant front teeth in the rear-view mirror to make sure they were free from lipstick.

She opened the door and started to get out. 'If she's non-susceptible, why's she bothering to go to a dentist who's a member of the Society of Medical Hypnotists?'

'Hold it a minute . . .' Through the gathering dusk, Ginzel had seen a man with a white poodle come out of the building next to Clair's. 'Well, if you do have trouble, I know where everything is,' he continued, as they watched the man make his way down towards the Embankment.

As soon as the man had turned the corner, Pierce strode confidently across the road and rang Clair's doorbell.

There was no reply. She waited a moment and rang again. This time she was rewarded by the sound of approaching footsteps. The door was opened as far as the security chain would allow, and Clair's face appeared.

Pierce smiled. 'Miss Tennant?'

She nodded.

'My name is Rossiter – Joanna Rossiter. I hope you'll forgive me for calling on you so late in the evening, but I'm a friend of Mrs Ibbotson – Esther's mother . . .'

Clair brightened; Esther Ibbotson had been one of her closest friends at art school. 'Really? I haven't seen Esther for – gosh! – I don't know how long . . . Must be a year at least. How is she?'

'Very well. You know, don't you, that she's had a daughter?'

'Yes, I do. I was heartbroken I couldn't get to the wedding, but at the time—' Clair stopped. 'Oh, I *am* sorry,' she said, lifting the security chain out of its slot. 'I'm being very rude – do please come in, Mrs Rossiter.'

Clair made coffee, and after they had spent ten minutes gossiping about the people and places they had in common, Pierce said: 'My dear, I've enjoyed our little chat so much I've almost forgotten what it was that brought me here in the first place! Do you think I might take up a minute more of your time?'

'Of course.' Clair refilled their cups. The flat always seemed very big and empty when Mike was away, and she was glad of the woman's company.

'I work for the Medical Research Council,' Pierce explained. 'I'm what is known as a research investigator.' She laughed. 'It

51

sounds frightfully sinister, doesn't it? Actually, it's not at all sinister . . . One of the things we're doing at the moment, with the help of the Department of Psychology at Reading University, is carrying out a study into the psychology of perception.

'Mrs Ibbotson knew this was something you were interested in, and suggested that I come along and see you. I gather it was the subject of a thesis you wrote while you were at the Royal College . . .'

'That's right.' Clair kicked off her open-toe sandals and curled her legs up under her. 'Do go on . . .'

For nearly fifteen minutes they talked enthusiastically about the project. 'What I'd like to do,' Pierce said finally, 'is have you take the tachistoscopic perception test. It really would be most interesting to see what results we get from someone with your artistic background.'

'Fine,' said Clair. 'What would I have to do?'

'Simply look at a series of images we'd put up on a tachistoscope – it's a thing rather like a slide projector, but one which allows you only a brief glimpse of what's on the screen. Afterwards, we'd ask you to describe what it was you saw – or thought you saw.' Pierce paused: an idea seemed to have occurred to her. 'As a matter of fact, I have one in the car . . .'

'In that case, why don't we do it now?'

Pierce turned and looked up at the schoolroom clock. 'You don't think it's too late?'

'Not for me it isn't,' Clair assured her. 'I'll tell you what: while you're getting it, why don't I make us some fresh coffee?'

Pierce returned several minutes later with a clipboard and the tachistoscope, which she placed on the table in front of the settee. The cable turned out not to be long enough to reach the nearest electricity socket, but this they solved simply by pushing the table and settee forward eighteen inches. Pierce switched on the tachistoscope, and then asked Clair to sit down in front of it. After a brief delay, a bright pin-point of light suddenly appeared in the middle of the screen.

'You might find it easier to see,' Pierce said, going around behind the settee to study the screen from Clair's viewpoint, 'if I switched off some of the lights. Would you mind?'

Clair said she wouldn't, and when Pierce returned she, too, sat down on the settee, her clipboard resting on her knees, and her handbag on the floor beside her.

'Good! Now the first thing I'd like you to do,' Pierce continued, 'is to make yourself as comfortable as possible. Just lie back – that's right – lie back and relax. Keep your eyes fixed on the screen and relax – that's *most* important! I shan't want you to do or say anything while you're watching the screen. Just relax and watch the screen. You may find yourself becoming drowsy, but that doesn't matter a bit. In fact, it's rather better if you do . . . So, just relax and watch the screen. Relax and watch the screen. That's really all there is to it. Relax and watch the screen.'

With her eyes fixed on the unwavering pin-point of light, Clair felt herself slowly becoming warm and sleepy – very sleepy. So sleepy that it became increasingly difficult for her to keep her eyes open. Although somewhere in her mind she knew that the spot of light on the screen had not changed, it appeared to be slowly expanding. As it expanded, the woman's voice began to recede. Now the whole room seemed to be filling with the light. Soon the effort of keeping her eyes open proved too much. And as she closed them, she felt some unidentifiable but vital part of herself float away into a timeless void.

For several minutes Pierce continued to repeat the command: 'Relax and watch the screen.' And then, in a voice that was to become progressively lower, slower and more monotonous, she said: 'I want you to listen carefully to what I say – your eyes are closed – you are feeling comfortable and relaxed – you are thinking of nothing but what I say – your arms and legs feel heavy and you are comfortable and relaxed – you are going backwards into the darkness, and as you go backwards into the darkness you feel more and more relaxed – breathing regularly and deeply, regularly and deeply – going into a deep, sound sleep – a deep, sound sleep. And as I count from one to ten your sleep will get deeper, much deeper.'

Slowly, Pierce began to count, and when she had finished she gently took hold of one of Clair's wrists, lifted her arm until it was level with her face, and then let it go. The girl's arm fell like that of a rag doll. She was in a state of deep hypnosis.

8

Although Clair could not open her eyes, the sweet, sickly smell of antiseptic told her she was in hospital. And that could only mean one thing: she was visiting her mother. Why then, had she believed her to be dead? She must have imagined it, she decided. A wave of relief spread through her; now all she had to do was open her eyes and everything would be all right.

'You ought to think about going soon, dear,' said her mother. 'It really isn't safe here . . .'

Clair smiled. For as long as she could remember, her mother's fear of germs had been a family joke. It was hardly surprising, therefore, that she should have thought the germ-laden atmosphere of a hospital unsafe.

As she leaned forward to kiss her mother goodbye, she felt her fingers brush against an iron bedstead and starched cotton sheets. 'All right, darling. But I'll be in to see you the same time tomorrow.'

She went to get up, but found that as well as being unable to open her eyes, she could not move her legs. She waited a moment, then tried again. Still she couldn't move.

Suddenly it struck her that it was *she* who was in bed – in bed and at home.

She would get up, she decided. Anything would be better than lying in the dark being tormented by such strange, sad dreams. And anyway, she was feeling thirsty – terribly thirsty.

Believing herself to be now wide awake, she tried to get out of bed. But still she could not move.

She swore, then tried again with greater determination. But no sooner had she succeeded in lifting herself up on to her elbow than she felt someone push her firmly back again. 'Lie still,' said a woman's voice, coming, it seemed, from the back of a deep, echoing cavern. 'Just lie still and everything'll be all right.'

Panic-stricken, Clair managed to force open her eyes. Peering down at her were several brown faces, one overlapping the other. The lips began to move in unison. 'You're in hospital,' the voice boomed. 'You've had an accident.'

Clair ran her tongue across her parched lips. 'An accident?'

Slowly, the faces began to merge until there was only one. 'I'm afraid so, honey. You fell down the stairs in your apartment. You've broken a leg and you're badly concussed.'

Clair lifted her head. Although still unable to focus properly, she could see that her left leg was lying in some sort of cradle held up by a complex arrangement of wires and pulleys attached to an overhead bar.

She fell back on to her pillow and closed her eyes, struggling to make sense of it all. She could remember returning home and going to answer the doorbell. Was it then she had fallen? It couldn't have been; she had been downstairs at the time, about to make herself coffee. But try as she might, she could remember nothing of what had happened after she had heard the bell. From then on, everything was a blank. Or was it? Although it made no sense to her, she could see herself packing, being driven to an airport and getting on board a plane. The journey seemed to have been a long one and had been followed by a sea crossing, during which a steel band had been playing . . .

What she was remembering, she decided, was another dream. A dream triggered, perhaps, by her journey in the ambulance.

With difficulty, she managed to ask the nurse which hospital she was in.

'St Stephen's,' she replied. 'St Stephen's in the Fulham Road.'

Reassured to find herself so near home, she gave up her struggle to stay awake and once again slipped into a sleep full of dreams more real than reality.

Clair had lost all concept of time, and the days or weeks or it may even have been months which followed were no more than a blur – a blur in which she was dimly aware of being washed and fed and given an endless sucession of tablets to swallow. From time to time people came to peer down at her and tell her that she was getting on fine, and that it wouldn't be long before she would be well enough to have visitors, watch television and read the papers.

On the few occasions she was able to organize her thoughts sufficiently to complain about her loss of memory and disorientation, she was told that they were nothing more than symptoms of concussion. Get plenty of rest and take your tablets, she was told, and everything will be just fine.

The suspicion that it was the tablets which were responsible for her disorientation grew slowly. Although it seemed to take her weeks to marshal the necessary strength and determination, she finally made up her mind to put the theory to the test. So, instead of obediently swallowing the next lot, she rolled them under her tongue. Then, pretending to have choked on the water with which she was supposed to have washed them down, she spat the tablets into a paper tissue and hid them beneath her pillow.

She lay back, closed her aching eyes and waited to see what would happen.

At first she felt no different. Still she seemed lost within the universe of her own body – a universe where time ebbed and flowed surrealistically, and where two and two no longer made four.

But then she noticed that she seemed at last to be repossessing her body.

Her head began to clear, and, for the first time, she was able fully to comprehend her room. It was small and white and lit with fluorescent strips. Apart from the bed, it contained only a locker, some intravenous stands and a couple of stacking chairs. Hanging on the facing wall was a dated-looking lithograph of the Houses of Parliament, and the windows were covered with dark-blue curtains. Although she supposed it to be a room in the private wing of St Stephen's, there was neither a television set nor a radio, no telephone, no mirror, no clock – not even a bedside lamp. Most curious of all, there were no flowers. Even if Mike hadn't been allowed in to see her, she knew he would have sent flowers.

Suddenly an appalling thought struck her: she had not been injured falling downstairs, but in a car crash – a crash in which

56

Mike had died. That was why he hadn't been to see her, or sent flowers. He was dead, and they were waiting until she had recovered sufficiently to be told.

And yet that didn't make sense. If *he* hadn't ararnged for her to be nursed in a private room, who had? And if there had been a car crash, why hadn't she suffered more extensive injuries? Puzzled, she turned back the sheet and lifted the hem of her white cotton gown. There was not a sign of a cut or a bruise anywhere. She raised her buttocks and began exploring her back and thighs. There was nothing wrong there either.

And there was another thing, she suddenly realized: if her leg was broken, why wasn't it in a cast?

Cautiously, she withdrew it from the cradle and began gently prodding it. It seemed to be perfectly all right.

Had she been in hospital so long that the break had mended? If it had, why was her leg still in a cradle?

It was then that she noticed that her legs were quite smooth. Had they been waxed? In *hospital*? It seemed hardly likely. In which case she could only have been there for a few days at most.

Something was wrong, terribly wrong. If she *had* only been there for a few days, she couldn't possibly have broken her leg.

Had they somehow managed to confuse her with another patient? A girl with the same name as herself, who really *did* have a broken leg? With the National Health Service now teetering on the verge of total collapse, such mix-ups were not unknown.

She got out of bed and began searching for a bell-push with which to summon a nurse, but there was none. Then, with her feet making small tacky sounds on the vinyl-covered floor, she crossed to the door and turned the handle. It was locked. She began hammering her fists on the door, but the quilting with which it was covered absorbed the sound totally

She looked around, frantically wondering what to do next. The window. Perhaps there was a fire-escape outside the window? She ran across the room and threw back the curtains.

She had expected to find herself looking down on the jumble of dingy houses and shops which flank the Fulham Road; to have seen lighted street-lamps and a dribble of cars and taxis, perhaps even a bus if it wasn't too late.

Instead, there were palm trees and bougainvillaea, pink sand and a glittering, peacock-blue sea.

As she began to scream, a cloud of brilliantly coloured birds rose from the palm fronds and wheeled away into a flawless sky.

9

Michael Fitzpatrick arrived back at his flat at 6.30 on the evening of August 19th. When he had spoken to Clair eight days
earlier, she had told him she was about to begin directing the
photography for a Christmas catalogue she had designed. He
had rung her several times since then, but had got no reply.
In the circumstances, he hadn't been surprised. Neither had he
been surprised when she hadn't been at the airport to meet
him: in his telegram he had said only that he *hoped* to be on
the 4.30 flight from Belfast.

He got out his keys and began unlocking the front door. It
was good to be back. His office wasn't expecting him until after
the weekend, and Clair had said she would be through with
everything by the time he returned. They would have a drink,
catch up on what had been happening, and then he would take
her to her favourite restaurant for dinner. After stopping at
one of the little riverside pubs near Battersea bridge, they would
return home and make love for much of the night.

'Clair,' he called, as he pushed the door open with his shoulder. 'Clair darling, it's—' He stopped; there were newspapers
and letters scattered all over the hall floor.

With a mounting sense of apprehension, he put down his
luggage and went through into the living-room.

'Clair?'

Except for the sound of a tap dripping in the kitchen, the
room was silent, and the air still and lifeless as a vault. The
clock had stopped, and several of the plants had begun to wilt.

And then he noticed the envelope that was propped against
a bowl of over-ripe fruit on the dining table.

Something was wrong. He picked it up, held it to the light for
a moment, then tore it open and unfolded the sheet of paper
inside.

Something was definitely wrong; *very* wrong. In the past,
most of her letters to him had been handwritten and peppered
with funny drawings. The one he was holding had been typed,

and there were no drawings. More chilling still, it began with the one word *Mike*.

He began reading: *I'm sorry to do this to you, but I've decided I just have to get away for a while – be by myself and think things through.*

The past eighteen months have been the best ever, and although you're not going to believe me, I still love you. But it's all become too cosy, too predictable. I feel I know what the next thirty years are going to be like, and for me that's very scary.

I realize this isn't going to be easy for you. But please believe me, it isn't easy for me either. That's why I didn't dare wait to tell you myself – you could have talked me out of going so easily. And in the long run, that wouldn't have been good for either of us. Please try and not hate me too much.

Dumbfounded, he looked around the room. She couldn't have gone, he told himself, her things were still here: her drawing table, her plan-chest and filing cabinet, her pictures and her books.

The letter was some kind of a joke; a bloody silly one, but a joke nevertheless.

Exasperated, he crossed to the foot of the stairs, called her name again, and then, when still there was no reply, raced up to the bedroom and threw open the door.

Although hot as an oven, it looked no different from when he had left. Neither did the bathroom; her white towelling robe was still there, so was her shower-cap. But what about the rest of her clothes?

He returned to the bedroom and slid aside the door of her wardrobe. Although there were boots and a great many pairs of shoes on the floor, most of the hangers were empty.

Suddenly on the verge of tears, he backed away until his legs encountered the side of the bed, sat down and began fumbling for a cigarette. It wasn't true; she couldn't have walked out – not like this. Or could she? She had, after all, been in a very strange mood just before he had left.

Aware that he had somehow managed to light the filter-tip end of the cigarette, he stubbed it out and looked again at her letter. *I'm sorry to do this to you, but I've decided I just have to get away for a while – be by myself and think things through.*

He could feel himself becoming angry. What kind of a stupid bastard did she think he was? For Christ's *sake*, she'd had two whole weeks by herself if she'd needed to think anything through.

There had to be another man. It was the only explanation which made any kind of sense. Wiping the tears from his cheek, he turned and stared stupidly down at the bed. Had the little bitch screwed the other guy in their bed? Viciously, he stripped back the counterpane, but the sheets were as unsullied as freshly fallen snow.

That proved nothing, he decided. She probably wouldn't have brought him here anyway – that would have made her feel too much like a whore.

With his face stiff with suppressed rage, he returned to the wardrobe and began going through the pockets of the clothes she had left behind. Somewhere there must be *something* that would give him a clue as to what had really happened. A telephone number on a scrap of paper, perhaps even a note. But apart from a couple of coins and a bus ticket, he found nothing.

He returned to the downstairs room and continued his frantic search. Although her cheque book, paying-in book and passport were missing, she seemed to have left everything else behind. Her address book was there, and more curious still, so was the book in which she kept specimens of her work.

Trembling, he poured himself a brandy and sat down. He had to collect his thoughts, think this thing through. If she had gone to another city, she would need her specimen book in order to get work. So why hadn't she taken it with her? Did it mean she only intended to be away for a few weeks, or had she, in her rush to leave, simply forgotten it? Probably the latter, he decided. In that case, first thing tomorrow morning he would get the locks changed. That way, if she wanted anything she would bloody well have to ask him for it.

Suddenly, the total improbability of the whole situation hit him. If anyone had told him fifteen minutes earlier that he would now be planning to change the locks he would have laughed. It could never happen, he'd have said. They had too much respect for each other. Okay, so it was always *theore-*

tically possible that one of them might meet someone they liked more, but if that happened they would handle it in a civilized manner. After all, they weren't simply *in* love, they actually loved each other. The distinction, he would have explained, was an important one. Love was total physical and mental rapport; being *in* love little more than a passing madness – a *folie à deux* in which each partner unwittingly acted out the wish-fulfilment fantasies of the other.

Well, he thought bitterly, it just goes to show how wrong you can be.

He got up, turned off the dripping tap and began opening windows. Outside, voices ebbed and flowed, making him still more aware of his own isolation. By the time he had finished, he had abandoned the idea of changing the locks. The fact that she had behaved like a bloody fool was no reason for him doing the same.

So, what *should* he do next? Start ringing her friends, he decided. One of them was bound to know what it was all about.

He refilled his glass and for almost an hour made one call after another. None of them knew anything.

It was now twilight. Although he wasn't feeling hungry, he decided he had better eat something. He went into the kitchen and switched on the lights. There was cheese and an unopened packet of ham in the refrigerator, but the bread was spotted with mould. He was about to toss it into the waste-bin when another thought occurred to him. The dustmen's strike. Of course; he'd read a story about it only a couple of days earlier. If there had been anything Clair hadn't wanted him to see, she would have put it in the dustbin, expecting it to have been emptied by the time he returned.

He went out into the yard and lifted the dustbin lid. As he had expected, it was full. However, by now it was almost too dark to see. So, after spreading newspapers on the kitchen floor, he humped the dustbin inside and upended it. Trying not to breathe too deeply, he began sifting through the rubbish.

He had almost decided he was wasting his time, when, among the egg shells and the tea bags and the laddered tights, he came across an envelope from the Institute of Preventive Medicine. Why the hell had the Institute of Preventive Medicine written to her? Frantically, he began searching for the letter. He found one piece, then another. Soon he had enough to know the answer: they had written to confirm an appointment she'd made for the day he had flown to Ireland.

At last he thought he understood: the screening had uncovered the fact that she was ill, perhaps even fatally ill (Hodgkin's Disease was the first idea that flashed into his mind). She had left because she hadn't wanted to be a burden to him.

Suddenly weighed down with guilt for the thoughts he'd had earlier, he shovelled the rubbish back into the bin and began washing his hands.

It wasn't going to be easy to find out what was in the Institute's report; they certainly weren't going to tell him, nor, probably, would her own doctor. However, he could only try; if, that is, he could remember the man's name.

Flinging aside the towel, he returned to the living-room and began working his way through her address book.

Dr Reischauer? No, it was the wrong address; her GP practised somewhere in South Kensington. He continued turning the pages, until, in the V section, he found what he had been looking for.

He picked up the telephone and dialled the number. It was engaged. Drumming his fingers impatiently, he waited a minute and tried again. This time he got an answering service. Well, that was that; there was nothing more he could do until the following morning.

After watering the plants, he took his cases upstairs and unpacked, putting the bottle of Yves St Laurent he had bought for her in one of the dressing-table drawers. Then, after setting the alarm clock for 7.30, he swallowed a Nembutal capsule and climbed into bed.

When, on the following morning, Fitzpatrick returned from seeing Clair's doctor, the flat seemed even more desolate than it had the night before. On his way back he had stopped at one of the supermarkets in the King's Road and bought himself some food for the long, empty weekend which lay ahead, and, after dumping it on the kitchen table, he put on the kettle. While waiting for it to come to the boil, he reviewed the situation in the light of what he had discovered – which wasn't much.

The doctor – a partner in a group practice near South Kensington underground station – had been sympathetic. After listening to Fitzpatrick, he had said: 'I'm sure Miss Tennant wouldn't mind my telling you that in all essential respects, the screening confirmed what I'd thought all along – that she's a remarkably healthy young woman.'

When Fitzpatrick asked him why she had wanted to have a screening, the doctor had shrugged. 'Probably because she was planning to leave. Patients often do become insecure about their health before embarking upon a major change of lifestyle.'

By now the kettle had begun to whistle. Still deep in thought, Fitzpatrick switched it off, put Nescafé and sugar into a mug and filled it with boiling water.

According to the letter from the Institute, Clair had phoned for an appointment at the end of July. So, if the doctor's interpretation was correct, she must have begun thinking about leaving at least a couple of weeks before that. Probably longer. The curious thing was that the first two weeks in July had been exceptionally happy. They had been to the theatre and the cinema, seen several exhibitions and spent an idyllic weekend in a cottage on the Norfolk coast. They had even left their names with a couple of estate agents, hoping to find a cottage they could afford to buy.

So, was her decision to leave anything to do with the fact that they hadn't married? It was possible, but not very likely. They had always agreed that there wasn't much point in marrying until they were ready to have children – something she didn't want to do for a couple more years yet.

Fitzpatrick finished his coffee and rinsed the mug, then went through to the living-room and began winding the clock.

The only thing he could remember her complaining about – and then only jokingly – was his cynicism. Like most successful journalists, he was, he knew, a bit of a hustler. You had to be. It was a tough, highly competitive business (Nicholas Tomalin – one of the folk heroes of Fleet Street – once said that the qualities essential for real success in journalism are ratlike cunning, a plausible manner, and a literary ability; although Fitzpatrick would have added insatiable curiosity and an unwillingness to take anything at its face value, it was, as far as it went, a good definition). Perhaps she really had come to dislike this streak in his personality. It was possible, but again, not very likely. After all, he had never behaved cynically towards her. And anyway, warm and gentle though she was, she could act like a real little Lizzie Borden if driven to it.

After turning the hands of the clock to 11.15, he set the pendulum swinging, then looked at her letter again.

Although the signature was undoubtedly hers, the phrasing was not. And there was something else odd about the letter: in the past she had only typed notes to him when in a hurry, and then she had used the same kind of reporter's shorthand as he used – t for the, tt for that, bn for been, and so on. But in this letter, all the words had been spelt in full.

He knew from the slight defect in the lower-case e that the letter had been typed on her machine; but had someone else typed it for her?

Earlier that year she had, he remembered, designed the jacket for a coffee-table book about fortune telling, and had used prints of both her left and her right hand. But had she yet received a proof? He began looking through her specimen book. She had. He took out the proof and examined it closely. Although the prints were slightly smaller than life-size, all of the friction-ridges had reproduced perfectly. So far so good. What he would do now was compare the fingerprints on the typewriter with those on the book jacket.

After fetching a tin of talcum powder from the bathroom, he began assembling the rest of the things he would need – a roll of Scotch tape, a magnifying glass and one of her sable brushes. When he had got them all together, he emptied a little of the talcum powder on to a sheet of paper, dipped the brush into it and carefully dusted the first of the typewriter keys. Under the magnifying glass he could see that the talc had adhered to the pattern of body-oil left behind when the key had last been struck. The next thing he had to do was lift the print and compare it with those reproduced on the book jacket. He tore off a two-inch strip of Scotch tape, pressed the sticky side firmly against the key he had just dusted, then stripped it off. Against the light, he saw that he had lifted an almost perfect print. Knowing that she typed with two fingers only, he compared it with the left-hand forefingers on the book jacket. They matched one another perfectly, each having the same comparatively rare tented arch.

There was, he knew, no point in repeating the process on all of the keys; in even such a short letter, many would have been struck over and over again, blurring the prints hopelessly. Instead, he went through the letter looking for characters which had been used only once. There were four: j, k, x and z. In theory, each should bear a latent print as good as the one he had lifted from the Q key (a character which, he now realized, hadn't been used in the writing of the letter).

One by one he dusted the keys, applied a length of Scotch tape and stripped it off. There was not even a fragment of a print on any of them.

So, what did it prove? That she had been wearing gloves when she'd typed the letter? In the middle of a *heatwave*?

He began to tap the end of the brush against his teeth. But supposing someone *else* had typed it, someone anxious not to reveal their identity. Might not they have worn gloves?

Although it seemed a ridiculously melodramatic idea, he couldn't rid himself of it. If someone *had* typed the letter for her, that person would almost certainly have left with her. In which case, there was just a chance that they would have been seen by one of the neighbours.

He got to his feet and began straightening his tie. If he drew a blank on this one, he would, he decided, give up.

But he did not draw a blank: one of his neighbours had seen the person with whom Clair had left, and the story he told was enough to convince Fitzpatrick that his next move should be to talk to Detective Inspector Reginald Atwell as soon as possible.

10

Fitzpatrick arrived at the Palace Gate entrance to Kensington Gardens at 2.30 the following afternoon, and, trying as far as he could to keep within the shade of the drought-stricken trees, set out across the brown, dusty grass in the direction of the Round Pond.

Fitzpatrick had first got to know Reginald Atwell five years earlier, when he had been a cub reporter with a West London weekly and Atwell a detective sergeant attached to F Division. At first, their relationship had been amicable but not all that close. But then Atwell's wife had been convicted of shoplifting. As sometimes happens, Fitzpatrick had been the only reporter in Uxbridge Magistrates Court on the morning her case had been heard. Aware that such a story would not only have been splashed in his own paper but picked up by the nationals as well, he had, as a favour to Atwell, decided not to file. Atwell had been deeply touched, and, although his marriage was not to last more than another year, the two men had become close friends.

Fitzpatrick emerged from the trees and picked his way through the sunbathers to join the crowds wandering along the path surrounding the Round Pond. Ducks swam between the model sailing ships becalmed on the huge sheet of metallic-looking water, and, high above, kites drifted listlessly in the stagnant air.

He eventually found Atwell on the north side of the pond, squatting on his heels examining one of his son's yachts. Like most men in the park on that brutally hot afternoon, he was wearing only a pair of shorts.

'Permission to come aboard, sir?'

'Mike!' Atwell straightened up, grimaced, and, after massaging his cramped thigh muscles for a moment, shook hands. 'Am I glad to see you, sunshine!' he said, thrusting the yacht into Fitzpatrick's hands. 'You know all about boats, don't you?'

'A bit. Why, what's the problem?'

As Atwell began to explain, his youngest son burst into tears. 'Billy busted it!'

'No I bleedin' didn't!' cried his brother. Like their father, both boys spoke with a Cockney accent.

'Oi!' said Atwell sternly. 'That's enough of that for a *start*!' His manner softened. 'Now, say hello to your Uncle Mike.'

Grudgingly, the boys did as they had been told.

Atwell turned back to Fitzpatrick. 'Sorry it had to be here,' he said under his breath. 'But it was my weekend to have the little perishers.'

With the aid of a nail-file Fitzpatrick managed to free the jammed tiller pivot and the yacht was handed back to the boys. Then, after promising them an ice-cream each in return for ten minutes' peace and quiet, their father led Fitzpatrick across to a pair of deckchairs, scooped up the shirt and sandals he had used as territorial markers, and they sat down. 'Here, do you want some of this?' he asked, holding up a bottle of Ambre Solaire.

'Not right now . . .'

Atwell shook out a palmful of the lotion and began rubbing it into his hairy chest. 'Well, it ain't exactly Majorca,' he said cheerfully, 'but it's a bloody sight better than being at the Nick!'

Clasping his hands behind his balding head, he stretched out contentedly. 'Right, my old son. So, what's your problem, then?'

'It's Clair . . .'

A sudden puff of wind ruffled the surface of the pond, bringing with it the far-away sound of a brass band playing 'After the Ball is Over'.

'Your bird?'

'My *ex*-bird . . .'

'Oh yeah,' said Atwell non-committally. 'What's she been getting up to?'

'She's gone missing.'

'Gone *missing*?' An undertone of suspicion had entered Atwell's voice. 'How do you mean, she's gone missing?'

Fitzpatrick reached into the back pocket of his slacks. 'When

I got back from Belfast on Friday I found this,' he said, handing him Clair's letter.

Atwell sat up and read it through carefully. 'Oh, Gawd!' he said, returning it to Fitzpatrick. 'Did you have any idea she was brewing up for something like this?'

'Not really . . .'

'Not *really*? What's that Chinese for?'

Fitzpatrick shrugged. 'We had a bit of a bumpy patch a couple of weeks ago, but that all got sorted out. No, it was fine – just fine.'

'Then why do a moonlight? Do you think she was having it off with another fella?' Atwell was a man who didn't believe in beating about the bush. 'I mean, with you away so much, she'd have had plenty of opportunity . . .'

'I'd be surprised – *very* surprised.'

Fitzpatrick told him about the phone calls he had made, the letter from the Institute of Preventive Medicine he had found in the dustbin, and his visit to her doctor. 'And then yesterday afternoon I decided to call on my neighbours, hoping that one of them had seen her leave. One of them had – a guy called de Souza in the block next door.

'The Friday before last, de Souza noticed a car parked across the road with a middle-aged couple sitting in it. This would have been about seven or so. They were still there when he took his dog out for a walk at nine, and he got it into his head that they might have been casing the place.'

'Did he call the Old Bill?'

'No, he didn't. The silly sod "didn't like to". Anyway, as he was getting ready to go to bed – and this would have been around 10.30 – he saw the guy come out of our place carrying two suitcases. A couple of minutes later Clair and the woman appeared, got into the car with the guy and drove off.'

'Did he get the number of the jam-jar?'

'You're kidding? Listen, he didn't even know what *make* of car it was! He said – and I quote – that it was "sort of small and green, with a little window in the roof"!'

Atwell brushed away a fly that had settled on his big belly. 'Sounds like a Ford Fiesta . . .'

'That's what I thought.'

'You know anyone with a Fiesta?'

Fitzpatrick shook his head.

'What about the couple? Do they sound like anyone you know?'

Fitzpatrick shook his head again. 'Nope.'

'Anything else?'

'That's about it . . .'

'It's not much, is it?' said Atwell gloomily. 'There's certainly no point in reporting any of this – with something like twenty thousand people a year going missing, the Woodentops wouldn't want to *know*.

'Of course,' he added, 'I suppose there's always the Sally Army . . .'

'What, for Clair?' Fitzpatrick shook his head. 'Reggie, I was wondering if there was any chance of you having a word with Social Security, maybe, or her bank?'

Atwell thought about it for a moment. 'Well, I suppose I could *try*,' he said without enthusiasm. 'But I don't think it's going to get us very far. Social Security's bleeding slow, and I'd be surprised if she's done anything about transferring her bank account yet, or even notifying them of a change of address. She wouldn't need to if she had a banker's card. She did have a banker's card, didn't she?'

'Yes; and American Express.'

'Well, there you go,' said Atwell, hopelessly.

'And I suppose checking-out passenger manifests isn't on either?'

Atwell drew in his breath sharply, as though he had touched something uncomfortably warm. 'Do you know how many planes and boats and hovercraft leave this country every day?' he asked rhetorically. 'And anyway, how do we know she's gone abroad?

'I suppose it just *might* be worth your while asking the Post Office for a list of calls made on your phone,' he suggested, after a pause. 'Tell 'em you think you've been over-charged. If you get a number coming up a lot, and it's one you don't—'

Atwell broke off to bellow a warning at his sons, who had begun trying to push each other into the water.

'Little sods!' he said, turning back to Fitzpatrick. 'Where were we?' His eyes suddenly widened. 'Hey, listen, I've just had an idea!' he announced. 'You remember I went to the States last year? Well, while I was there I spent some time with the Los Angeles Police Department, looking at the work of their Svengali Squad—'

'Their *what*?' asked Fitzpatrick.

Atwell looked faintly embarrassed. 'Their Hypnosis Squad.' He waved his hand vaguely. 'I know it sounds a bit airy-fairy, but hang about. They've found, for example, that identikit pictures put together by witnesses who've been hypnotized are a hell of a lot more accurate than you'd normally expect. Also – and this is the real point – witnesses who at first thought they could remember bugger-all were able, under hypnosis, to read the registration numbers of suspects' cars and Christ knows what else!'

Fitzpatrick raised his eyebrows approvingly. 'And you're thinking—'

'Right!' exclaimed Atwell. 'That we hypnotize your mate—' He began snapping his fingers impatiently, not quite able to remember the man's name.

'De Souza,' said Fitzpatrick. 'Wilfred de Souza. Though I wouldn't exactly call him a *mate* . . .'

'Witness, then. We hypnotize your witness and see if he can come up with the number of the car Clair left in. Do you think he'll play ball?'

'I don't see why not,' replied Fitzpatrick, with more confidence than he felt. 'But who do we get to hypnotize him?'

Atwell's face clouded over. 'That's a point . . .'

'Do you have anyone at the Yard?'

'We don't. Or at least not yet. The DPP's worried that if we start fooling around with hypnosis we'll be accused of trying to *plant* information on witnesses, not get it out of them . . .'

A large red setter suddenly appeared from behind the deck-chairs, scattering the pigeons which had been strutting and crooning on the parched grass.

Atwell shooed it away. 'Bloody dogs,' he grumbled. 'They all want shooting. Do you know how much crap dogs deposit on London each day?' His voice rose. 'Sixty-six *tons*! Each day!'

'Really?' Fitzpatrick tried to sound suitably shocked. 'Listen, Clair's dentist is a hypnotist. I've never met him, but—' He paused. 'Wait a minute! I've got a better idea. I know a shrink called Gerhard Pohl who's *also* into hypnosis. I've used him several times on stories with a psychiatric angle, and he's always been very helpful.

'If I can get the two of them together, would you be prepared to sit in on the session?'

'Sure!' replied Atwell, without hesitation. 'By the way,' he added as an afterthought, 'what sort of guy is de Souza?'

Fitzpatrick shrugged. 'He's all right . . .'

'All right?' Atwell gave him a sidelong glance. 'There's something you're not telling me, isn't there?'

'What makes you think that?'

'It's called "street sense". So, let's be having you . . .'

'Well, de Souza's a bit . . .'

'A bit "Hello Sailor"?' Atwell groaned. 'That's *all* we need!'

'It's only the half of it; he also runs a dog's beauty parlour in Knightsbridge.'

'Yes?' said the voice from the entryphone.

Fitzpatrick put his lips close to the instrument and spoke. 'Mr de Souza?'

'Yes . . .' the voice replied cautiously.

'Mr de Souza, it's Michael Fitzpatrick. Michael Fitzpatrick from next door . . .'

The voice brightened. 'Oh yes! Do come up!'

De Souza was waiting at the door of his flat when Fitzpatrick emerged from the lift at the second floor. He was tall and willowy, with blue-rinsed wavy hair and the face of an ageing matinée idol. A striped butcher's apron was tied around his middle, and cradled in his arms was a miniature white poodle wearing a diamanté collar.

'I was just in the middle of making jam,' he explained, speaking in short, nervous rushes. 'Peach and almond. Have you ever tried it?'

Fitzpatrick said he hadn't.

'Then you must let me give you a jar,' said de Souza, leading him through a bead curtain into a room filled with Art Deco furniture. 'Even though I say it myself, it's rather delicious.'

Lying on a sofa covered with apricot-coloured raw silk was a much younger man with fair curly hair and a body-builder's physique.

'Charles, this is Mr Fitzpatrick. The young man I was telling you about.'

Charles lowered a copy of the *Sunday Times* Magazine from in front of his face and surveyed Fitzpatrick from head to foot. 'Hi,' he drawled, and then went back to his reading.

Fitzpatrick sat down.

'I don't know if I was of much help the other evening,' said de Souza, offering him a cigarette from a large mirrored box with a satinwood lining.

After assuring him that he had been of enormous help, Fitzpatrick explained what he wanted him to do next.

'Me? Be hypnotized?' De Souza lit his cigarette and began to puff it nervously, the way Bette Davis used to in her early films. 'Oh, I don't think I could do anything like *that*! Not be *hypnotized*.' He twisted around to look at the man on the settee. 'What do you think, Charles?' he asked. 'About me being hypnotized? Do you think I *ought* to?' He made it sound as if it were some sort of surgical operation.

'Suit yourself,' Charles replied, without looking up.

De Souza turned back to Fitzpatrick. 'But I don't know if I'd be any *good* at it,' he said, hoping that this would get him off the hook.

'I'm sure you would. Artistic people with high IQs usually make excellent subjects.'

Charles sniggered, but de Souza pretended not to notice. 'Really!' he said, suddenly a lot happier. 'Is that so? Well, of course, I'd be prepared to give it a go . . .'

'Great!' Fitzpatrick took out a notebook and began writing Pohl's address.

'I've just thought of something terrible,' de Souza announced, leaning across to tap Fitzpatrick on the knee. 'What happens if all my darkest secrets come tumbling out while I'm under the influence? Just *imagine*!'

'You'll send everyone else in the room into a deep sleep, ducky!' said Charles, without missing a beat.

Fitzpatrick tore the sheet off his pad and handed it to de Souza. 'Now, which evening would suit you best?'

De Souza bounded across to his writing table and switched on a lamp shaped like an arum lily. 'This week's not good,' he sighed, making a great show of leafing through a leather-bound diary. 'And next week's worse . . .' He turned to Charles. 'Are you going to Roddy's party on Wednesday?'

'Probably. Why?'

'Do you think he'll be *frightfully* upset if I don't?'

Charles shrugged. 'I shouldn't think he'll even notice . . .'

De Souza gave him a withering look. 'Thank *you*!' He turned back to Fitzpatrick. 'Well, shall we say next Wednesday evening then?'

11

'Snaith's coming *here*?' said Claude Ducasse, far too loudly. Dropping his voice almost to a whisper, he looked apprehensively around the crowded conference table. 'Now? This *afternoon*?'

Lee Quintrell nodded grimly. 'Tennant tried to make a break for it . . .' Quintrell – a serious-faced young man wearing horn-rimmed glasses and a dark-blue business suit – was operational head of what was known as the Ways and Means Committee of the Abaco Research Foundation, and it was the Ways and Means Committee which was responsible for the abduction, management and presentation of donors.

'Holy *shit*!' said Ducasse, taking half-a-dozen reels of film out of his document case and handing them to a waiting technician. He pushed the case out of sight beneath the table and sat down. 'So, what happened?' A nervous tic had appeared at the side of his lean, hawk-like face.

An elderly woman wearing a starched white coat and a hearing-aid explained.

'But why was she left alone?' asked Ducasse. His tic had got worse. 'That was a pretty dumb thing to have done.'

'The nurse's story was that she had a headache and went to the pharmacy for some codeine. Except when we tested her, we found she was full of amphetamine.'

Ducasse groaned.

'He had *his* ass reamed,' continued the woman, with a nod in the direction of Quintrell, 'I had my ass reamed, and the Mancini transplant will have to be put back until her bruises have cleared.'

Ducasse looked baffled. 'Until the *nurse*'s bruises have cleared?'

'Tennant's bruises!' hissed the woman. 'She was badly bruised while they were restraining her.'

'And the nurse? What's happened to the nurse?'

The woman put her forefinger to her throat and made a cutting motion.

'Wow!' Ducasse pulled a long face. 'That was a bit rough, wasn't it?'

'We couldn't go on using her popping pills the way she was, and the Old Man thought it wasn't safe to let her go.' The woman shrugged. 'So, that was that . . .'

Quintrell leaned forward, his elbows on the table. 'I think it was more a case of *pour encourager les autres,*' he told Ducasse. 'Ever since the business with Tennant he hasn't trusted anyone to tell him the goddamned time! I kid you not, he's been impossible . . .'

'Absolutely impossible,' echoed Pierce.

Quintrell pushed his glasses tight against the bridge of his nose. 'Did you hear about the chick on the cephalic transplant project?' he asked, looking around the table. Only the woman with the hearing-aid nodded.

'Well—' Quintrell paused to glance over his shoulder at the door '—this chick had a specimen develop cerebral oedema on her—'

'It happens,' said Ducasse, with a resigned shrug.

'Sure it happens. It happens all the time. That's what she tried to tell the Old Man. But boy, oh boy!' Quintrell closed his eyes tightly for a moment, as if trying to shut out a disagreeable sight. 'I kid you not, when he'd finished with her, the poor bitch was so freaked out she had to be given intravenous Valium! And you know something else—'

'Hold it a minute!' said Pierce, crossing to answer a telephone which had begun to ring.

'Hello?' The room fell silent. 'Yes, I'll tell him.' She replaced the receiver and returned to her seat. 'That was to say that the Old Man's tied up in Pathology,' she announced. 'He wants us to start without him.'

A sigh of relief went around the table.

'Okay!' said Quintrell brightly. 'So, let's get the show on the road!' He picked up his copy of the agenda, cleared his throat and began reading aloud. 'Item One: the Mancini heart transplant. Any problems with Tennant?' he asked Pierce.

'I don't think so . . .'

'And you're holding her – where? – in a cabin on Little Hippocrates?'

Pierce nodded. 'I've implanted her with a post-hypnotic suggestion that she's on holiday, waiting to be joined by her boyfriend.'

'And she's happy?'

'Perfectly happy.'

Quintrell shook his head regretfully. 'It's a pity we didn't do that in the first place.'

'If I'd known she was *that* good a subject, we would have done,' grumbled the woman with the hearing-aid.

'Quite so,' said Quintrell, before Pierce – who had given the woman a dirty look – had a chance to speak. 'Now, where have we got to with the plan to spoil—' He corrected himself. 'With the rationalization?'

In order to meet the necessary medical and legal requirements, donors had to be presented as bona fide accident victims. Each accident had therefore to be contrived in such a way that the donor's abdominal organs were undamaged although their brain was dying. This highly sophisticated form of murder – what Snaith insisted on calling 'rationalizations' – had in the past been achieved by a variety of methods including simulated suicides, drug overdoses, drownings and falls from high places.

Rationalizations were the responsibility of Ducasse and Ginzel, and, at the previous meeting of the Ways and Means Committee, they had tabled a plan for making it appear as if Clair had sustained her injuries while hang-gliding.

Quintrell, however, had not been happy. It was time, he had said, that they widened their repertoire to include accidents involving motor vehicles. 'Hell, we can't go *on* bucking the trend.'

Ginzel had resisted the suggestion, arguing that an auto accident would be both difficult to set up, and, since Clair Tennant rarely drove in London, inappropriate.

'Okay,' Quintrell had said, 'then make it look like she's the victim of a hit-and-run driver.'

But the Foundation's lawyer had advised against such a rationalization. 'I must remind the Committee that the Bill stating that a patient can be declared dead once it has been determined that irreversible cessation of brain function has occurred has not yet been tested in the context of a criminal case,' he had said. 'It's possible, therefore, that the District Attorney's office will object to Tennant being used as a donor, their argument being that if and when they bring the hit-and-run driver to trial he would plead that it wasn't *he* who killed Tennant, but the surgical team who removed her heart.'

Quintrell had accepted the lawyer's point, but, in spite of Ginzel's protests, had insisted that he and Ducasse prepare a rationalization based on a single-vehicle accident.

Ginzel was the first to speak. 'Well, we've put together a package,' he began without enthusiasm. 'But it's complicated and expensive.'

Quintrell looked enquiringly at Ducasse.

'The trauma profile *is* more elaborate than usual,' he warned. 'Even so, I'm not too worried.'

Ginzel, in the meantime, had begun passing out sheaves of mimeographed sheets.

'What the hell's *this*?' Quintrell demanded, flipping through the set which had been handed to him.

Ginzel explained that it was a cost analysis of mounting the rationalization.

'Wouldn't it make more sense if we heard what we're supposed to be getting for our money first?' It was a long agenda, and Quintrell – a graduate of the Harvard Business School – was more than usually anxious that the meeting should proceed in an orderly, efficient manner. 'Now stop being a pain in the ass, and get on with the presentation!' he said, thrusting the cost analysis to one side.

Ginzel picked up the remote-control switch that was lying on the table in front of him and pressed a button. The electrically operated Venetian blinds closed, and a moment later a map of Coral Gables appeared on the screen at the end of the darkened room.

'Okay, the rationalization is scheduled to take place in seventeen days' time. The scenario is this: it's one minute past midnight on the morning of September 9 and Tennant's driving back to her motel in West Miami. She's heading west along Sevilla Avenue. As she rounds De Soto Fountain—' he pressed another button and the lens zoomed in on an area above the South Dixie Highway '—the front offside tyre blows, she loses

78

control and runs smack into one of the bollards around the Fountain.'

The map was replaced by a colour photograph of the Spanish fountain. In the background, rising above the palms which encircled the spacious plaza, was the tower of what had once been the Hotel Miami Biltmore.

'Apart from the fact that De Soto Fountain is only a couple of minutes away from Coral Gables Hospital,' Ginzel continued, 'at that hour in the morning it's pretty well deserted.'

'Who, then, calls for the ambulance?' asked Quintrell.

Ginzel nodded at a man seated to the right of Ducasse. 'A couple Cahill's got lined up,' he replied. 'They're going to be okay – a retired bank teller and his wife. Moved to Miami from Pittsburgh a couple of years back. Solid, respectable senior citizens.'

'Where did you find them?' Quintrell asked Cahill. 'And more to the point, why have a couple of solid, respectable senior citizens agreed to involve themselves in a heavy number like this?'

'A buddy of mine over at the West Flagler Kennel Club put me on to them,' Cahill explained. 'They've been out of luck all season, and jumped at the chance of earning themselves a thousand bucks.'

'How much did you have to tell them?'

'Only that on their way home from dinner and a movie they'll have to call an ambulance for a girl injured in an accident . . .'

'H'm,' said Quintrell, non-committally. He turned back to Ginzel. 'And how do you propose to crash the automobile?'

'We've already crashed it,' he replied, to the surprise of everyone except Ducasse and Cahill. 'It was the only way we had of knowing what injuries to inflict on Tennant. So, we cast ourselves an exact replica of one of the bollards around the Fountain and ran it into that . . .'

Ginzel passed the remote-control switch to Ducasse. 'I guess maybe you'd better take up the story from here on in . . .'

'Hold it a minute!' said Quintrell. 'If you've already crashed it, how're you going to get it to the Fountain, for chrissake?'

'By truck. We spoil Tennant and put her into it on the way there. But let Claude give you the blow-by-blow.'

79

'Okay, but I'll be coming back to you,' Quintrell warned.

Ducasse had once been a plastic surgeon with a formidable reputation for rebuilding the faces of patients disfigured by cancer. Fearing the consequences of the separatist movement in Canada, he had emigrated to the United States in 1977, where he had got to know Snaith while practising in Houston.

At first, all had gone well with him; that is, until he had suddenly found himself in court charged with gross neglect and professional incompetence that endangered life.

The claimant's predatory lawyer had enjoyed a field day with Ducasse's admittedly extravagant life-style, picturing him as a playboy too dissipated to hold a steady scalpel. Heavy damages had been awarded, and – inadequately covered by malpractice insurance – he had ended up deeply in debt. More serious still, his licence had been revoked by the State Medical Board. Disgusted by what he insisted was a miscarriage of justice, he had left for the West Coast, where he had eked out a living treating unreported gunshot wounds.

Although it had taken Snaith a long time to track him down, it had been worth it. For as well as possessing the necessary surgical skills, he had by then acquired the kind of underworld contacts that both Snaith and Quintrell lacked, and it was he who had recruited Ginzel and Cahill.

Ducasse reached into the pocket of his hacking jacket, took out a pipe and began to fill it from a pigskin tobacco-pouch. 'Paul's only partially right when he says we had to crash the automobile *before* we knew what injuries we'd have to inflict,' he began. 'In fact, I'd already subjected a computer model of Tennant – programmed from a photogrammetric scan of the girl's body – to a range of decelerative forces before the crash. This was necessary in order to establish the *minimum* speed at which she'd have to be travelling in order to sustain injuries consistent with brain-death. The next step was to see what happened to an anthropomorphic model when we crashed the automobile for real.'

Ducasse paused to put a match to his pipe. 'If anyone's interested,' he added, as the aromatic smoke began to drift down the table, 'I've brought the film of the crash with me . . .'

'How long does it run?' asked Quintrell, looking anxiously

at his wristwatch. 'I mean, like we're not going to have to send out for popcorn, are we?'

'The Real Time was three hundred milliseconds, but it was shot in slow motion so I suppose we're talking about – what? – a little over three minutes.'

'Hardly a main feature.' Quintrell relaxed. 'Fine, then let's run it.'

Ducasse pressed a button on the remote-control switch and a picture of a blue Volkswagen appeared on the screen. Strapped into the driver's seat was a fully clothed model of Clair.

'If this is the one which is to be used on the night, why has the passenger door been removed?' asked Quintrell.

Ducasse blew a smoke ring at the ceiling. 'Simply in order to study what happens to the model on impact. It's since been re-hung, suitably deformed. The VW, by the way, is travelling at forty-two miles per hour. Needless to say, the last thing we want is for Tennant to die on the way to hospital. So, as I explained a couple of minutes back, it was a question of going for the lowest speed that could reasonably be expected to lead to brain-death.'

'And what about the real bollard?' asked Quintrell. 'The one at De Soto Fountain. How're you going to make it look as if it's been hit by an automobile travelling at forty miles an hour?'

'We know from the test that it's the vehicle which takes the punishment, not the bollard. What has to be done to the bollard can be done in a few minutes on the night,' replied Ducasse.

'Incidentally,' he added, before settling down to watch, 'we chose a VW for its rear-mounted engine. Obviously the engine has to be warm when the police arrive, and one mounted in front might have been so badly damaged by a head-on collision that we wouldn't have been able to start it on the night.'

By now the Volkswagen was beginning to wrap itself slowly around the reinforced concrete bollard. Like a figure in a nightmare, the dummy began to rise up from the driver's seat, its arms flailing. Soon, its head and shoulders were enveloped in a kaleidoscope of slowly turning fragments of windshield glass. As the vehicle's bodywork continued to crumple, the dummy's knees disappeared beneath the dashboard and its head began to plough into the upper edge of the windshield.

'You'll notice that although the seat belt is stopping her from actually going out through the windshield, her thorax and abdomen are taking a lot of punishment from the steering wheel,' said Ducasse, his eyes still fixed on the screen. 'However, providing we inflict severe bruising, I don't feel there's any need to break bones – at least not in her ribcage.'

By now, everything was beginning to settle down, and, with the tattered dummy wallowing back on to its seat, the end leader began to race through the gate.

'Right,' said Quintrell. 'Now maybe you'd take us through the trauma profile.'

An annotated, computerized representation of a woman's body appeared on the screen, and Ducasse crossed to stand alongside it. 'Starting from the top and working down,' he said, using the stem of his pipe as a pointer. 'Impact with the edge of the windshield will cause a laceration to the forehead. The superior edge of the laceration will be turned under, the inferior edge shelved away, and there will be a fracture of the skull subjacent to the laceration.

'Deceleration forces will cause lesions of the inferior surfaces of the frontal lobes, the formation of an acute subdural haematoma and contusional brain swelling, which in turn will lead to progressive lateral displacement of the brain, herniation of the hippocampal gyrus—'

'Yes, yes, yes!' said Quintrell, irritably. 'But what does it all *mean*?'

'It means that if everything works according to plan, by the time they've got her into a neurosurgical ward, removed the intracranial clot and reduced the tentorial herniation, so much ischaemic damage will have been done that it'll only be a matter of days before she's formally declared to be brain-dead.'

'And you're certain about that?' asked Quintrell.

Ducasse shrugged. 'You can never be 100 per *cent* certain about these things, but if it doesn't quite work out we can always do what we did in the Svensson case – have one of my people put on a nurse's uniform, slip into the hospital and pinch off an IV line or something. With so many float nurses on duty the whole time, getting in and out'll be no sweat.

'Anyway, to continue . . .' Ducasse turned back to the screen. 'Impact with the steering wheel will result in extensive contusions of the chest and abdomen, although as I said earlier, we'll be taking care to avoid compression fractures of the ribs.

'Impact with the dashboard will cause lacerations and abrasions to both knees, shattering of the right knee-joint and fracture of the right femur.

'Finally, entanglement with the pedals will be indicated by longitudinal lacerations and abrasions on the dorsum of the right foot and toes.'

'That seems all pretty convincing,' said Quintrell. 'Though for God's sake watch those abdominal contusions – the Old Man thinks he may have a client for her Fallopian tubes.

'Now, how are you planning to inflict these injuries?'

Ducasse nodded at Ginzel, and an exploded isometric projection of a ten-wheeled truck – the kind used for transporting refrigerated meat – appeared on the screen. Although from the outside it appeared in no way out of the ordinary, inside it had been furnished like a cross between a garage workshop and a dental surgeon's operating suite. At one end of the rig was a Volkswagen standing on a set of ramps, and at the other an elaborate-looking chair surrounded by an assortment of medical equipment.

Ducasse smiled. 'Now you see where the money will be going,' he said. 'However, the thing to remember is that if auto-accident rationalizations become a regular feature, we'll be able to spread the capital costs . . .'

'Quite so,' said Quintrell. 'But do let's get on.'

Ducasse apologized. 'Would you put up the trauma unit,' he called to Ginzel. 'Just the trauma unit . . .'

After a couple of false starts, a drawing of the chair appeared on the screen. It was now possible to see that it was mounted on a track, and that it faced a panel containing a section taken from the upper edge of a car's windshield, a portion of dashboard, a steering wheel and a set of foot pedals.

'Tennant is strapped into the chair, which is propelled by compressed air along the track to this unit here,' explained Ducasse, pointing to the panel containing fitments from the interior of a car. 'All of the driver-impact sites – dashboard, steering wheel, etcetera – come from an identical VW to the one she's supposed to have been driving, and each is mounted independently. In that way, we're able to make very fine adjustments to the loadings on the various parts of her body.'

Quintrell reached across for a Thermos jug and poured a little iced water into a glass. 'I'm sorry, but I'm not sure I'm quite with you . . .'

'Let me give you an example: we know that if Tennant's rib-cage were to be crushed, there'd be a risk of pulmonary haemorrhage. Worse still, the heart itself could be damaged. To ensure that this doesn't happen, the steering column will be hydraulically mounted.'

Ducasse paused to relight his pipe. 'The only thing we can't be sure about at the moment is bleeding. Ideally, we'd like her not to begin to bleed until she's in the VW and on site. We know that hypnosis has been used to reduce bleeding following the extraction of teeth from haemophiliacs, but what we *don't* know is whether such an inhibition will survive traumatic shock. If we found it didn't, would you be *very* worried if we used a thromboplastin preparation to increase temporarily the efficacy of the natural clotting factors?'

'Does anyone have any views on that?' Quintrell asked, looking around the table.

'They're hardly likely to test for anything quite so recherché as thromboplastins,' said the woman with the hearing-aid. 'I'd have thought the main thing was to be sure you obliterate the needle puncture.'

'We'd use a high-pressure syringe.'

'Ah!' The woman smiled. 'But of course! Claude, I've got one small suggestion – might it not be a good touch if you were to remove the great toenail of the right foot to suggest hyperflexion at the moment of impact?'

Ducasse nodded. 'It's certainly worth thinking about. I'm just not sure whether such an injury would be consistent with the relatively low speed. However, I'll check it out . . .'

Throughout the latter part of Ducasse's presentation, Pierce had been growing more and more pale. Now, with the talk of removing a toenail from Clair's foot, she suddenly clapped a hand to her mouth and rushed out of the room.

'Oh *dear!*' said the woman with the hearing-aid. 'Don't tell me Mrs Pierce has become emotionally involved again?'

Quintrell shrugged. 'It's nothing that her share of Mancini's fee won't cure,' he said, settling down to examine the cost analysis.

12

Fitzpatrick sprinted up the front steps of the large, elegantly proportioned terrace house in Harley Street, looked down the array of polished brass name-plates and pressed the button beside the one engraved *Dr Gerhard H. Pohl. Private Residence.*

The door was opened a couple of minutes later by an elderly, white-haired man with a neatly trimmed beard. In spite of the stifling heat, he was wearing a heavy tweed suit, a wool shirt and tie, and a cardigan.

'Ah, Mr Fitzpatrick!' said Pohl, with a German accent. 'Do please come in.'

Fitzpatrick apologized for being a little late, but Pohl dismissed it with a wave of the hand. 'Mr de Souza's just rung to say he won't be here until eight,' he explained, motioning Fitzpatrick towards the waiting lift. 'Some trouble at the shop, I gather.'

Pohl squeezed in beside him and slammed the gate. With the crash still reverberating through the empty house, he pressed the top button and they began slowly to ascend. 'Now tell me, have there been any developments since we last talked?'

Fitzpatrick shook his head. 'Checking out the numbers called on our phone led absolutely nowhere, and there's been no response to the ads I put in the personal column of *The Times*.

'In fact, I'm beginning to get the nasty feeling that I'm in one of those situations where whatever I do I can't win. If we don't come up with something this evening I've had it; if we do and I find her, she's going to think me a pretty devious bastard for having used such methods.'

'You think she'll regard them as being – how do you say? – not quite cricket?'

'She's bound to . . .'

'We'll see,' said Pohl, as the lift came to a juddering halt. 'I know it may seem somewhat Arthurian but, you know, it's just possible that she was motivated by an unconscious wish to test the depth of your feeling for her.

the gate, 'how you
nd her.'

itzpatrick was led
ved Edwardian fur-
abinets, occasional
by grand crowded
anging on the yel-
of place in such a
mber of primitive

ained. 'That one—'
s that was hanging
by a young woman
enic. Very sad case

nd of a toilet being
into the room.
at can I get you to

ost interesting chat
is Squad,' said Pohl,
resting.' He refilled
n.
ginning to fan him-
and Social Psycho-
e been rabbiting on
s, I don't have the
just what the hell *is*

he said, taking an
pocket. 'I can tell
work, but precious
ox, he opened it and
er to one nostril and
xplained, wiping his
hief. 'Mr Churchill's
nch?'

'I should perhaps first exp...

derived from the Greek *hypn*... ...

very little if anything to do wit... ...

'When I hypnotize a patien... ...

is narrow, or, if you like, *misd*... ...

he paused, trying to think of...

chendieb?' he said, looking ov...

who steals from the pocket?'

'A pickpocket.'

Pohl smiled. 'Ah, yes! A pic... ...

to misdirect my patient's atten... ...

directs his victim's attention t...

his wallet.

'So I begin by asking him t... ...

thoughts. I then tell him that...

feeling heavy – so heavy that he... ...

open, and so on.

'Now once my patient accep... ...

– and remember he's lying com... ...

he's only one step away from...

heavy. Once he has accepted t...

accept that he can no longer ke...

eventually he will accept *any* su... ...

'Which is precisely why,' he...

sip of his drink, 'stage hypnosis...

since 1952.'

Atwell looked worried. 'You... ...

any suggestion a hypnotist cares...

sir, surely this isn't true? What...

to do something that would vio... ...

ciples?'

'He would do it!' replied Pol... ...

tion. 'You understand, of cour...

subjects who are susceptible to... ...

'But let me ask you a quest... ...

Atwell over the top of his glasse...

painful way of doing away with...

'Go ahead and surprise me . . ...

'Persuade it that chloroform...

'In which case,' he added, as he opened the gate, 'how you find her won't matter, just as long as you find her.'

After climbing a short flight of stairs, Fitzpatrick was led into a room filled with heavy, ornately carved Edwardian furniture. There were glass-fronted china cabinets, occasional tables made from elephants' feet, and a baby grand crowded with faded photographs in silver frames. Hanging on the yellowing walls, and looking curiously out of place in such a formidably bourgeois setting, were a number of primitive paintings.

'All done by former patients,' Pohl explained. 'That one—' he pointed at a picture of burning bodies that was hanging above the mantelpiece '—that one was done by a young woman who set fire to her parents' bed. Schizophrenic. Very sad case – they were in it at the time . . .'

From somewhere nearby came the sound of a toilet being flushed, and a moment later Atwell strode into the room.

'Now, Mr Fitzpatrick,' said Pohl, 'what can I get you to drink? A gin and tonic, perhaps?'

'Gin and tonic would be fine.'

'Mr Atwell and I have been having a most interesting chat about the work of the Los Angeles Hypnosis Squad,' said Pohl, handing Fitzpatrick his drink. 'Most interesting.' He refilled Atwell's glass and the three men sat down.

'You know something?' said Atwell, beginning to fan himself with a copy of the *Journal of Abnormal and Social Psychology*, 'I've just realized that although I've been rabbiting on about hypnosis for the past ten minutes, I don't have the foggiest idea what it actually is! I mean, just what the hell *is* hypnosis?'

Pohl chuckled. 'I only wish I knew!' he said, taking an antique silver snuff-box from his cardigan pocket. 'I can tell you what I *think* it is and how it *seems* to work, but precious little else.' After tapping the lid of the box, he opened it and put a pinch of the aromatic yellow powder to one nostril and then the other. 'Golden Cardinal,' he explained, wiping his nose with a red-patterned snuff handkerchief. 'Mr Churchill's favourite. Would anyone care to try a pinch?'

No one did.

'I should perhaps first explain that although the word is derived from the Greek *hypnos,* meaning sleep, in fact it has very little if anything to do with sleep.

'When I hypnotize a patient, what I'm endeavouring to do is narrow, or, if you like, *misdirect* his attention rather as a—' he paused, trying to think of the correct English word. *'Taschendieb?'* he said, looking over his glasses at Fitzpatrick. 'One who steals from the pocket?'

'A pickpocket.'

Pohl smiled. 'Ah, yes! A pickpocket!' He began again. 'I try to misdirect my patient's attention rather as a pickpocket misdirects his victim's attention by bumping into him as he lifts his wallet.

'So I begin by asking him to clear his mind of extraneous thoughts. I then tell him that he is tired, that his eyelids are feeling heavy – so heavy that he is no longer able to keep them open, and so on.

'Now once my patient accepts the suggestion that he *is* tired – and remember he's lying comfortably in a dimly lit room – he's only one step away from accepting that his eyelids feel heavy. Once he has accepted that, it is easier still for him to accept that he can no longer keep them open, and so on, until eventually he will accept *any* suggestion I care to put to him . . .

'Which is precisely why,' he added, after pausing to take a sip of his drink, 'stage hypnosis has been illegal in this country since 1952.'

Atwell looked worried. 'You say that a patient will accept any suggestion a hypnotist cares to put to him. But with respect, sir, surely this isn't true? What if you were to ask your subject to do something that would violate his moral and ethical principles?'

'He would do it!' replied Pohl, without a moment's hesitation. 'You understand, of course, that we are talking about subjects who are susceptible to hypnosis . . .

'But let me ask you a question,' he continued, looking at Atwell over the top of his glasses. 'What is the easiest and least painful way of doing away with a cat?'

'Go ahead and surprise me . . .'

'Persuade it that chloroform kills fleas! You smile, my

friend, but let me give you an example of what I mean. God forbid, but let us say that I have hypnotized a nun, and I want her to take off her clothes in front of an audience of young men. What would I do? I would suggest to her that it is an uncomfortably warm day, that she is alone on a deserted beach, and that to disrobe would be wonderfully cooling and would involve her in no impropriety whatsoever . . .'

Pohl crossed one leg over the other. 'You know, during the last war some of the agents we put into occupied Europe were given their cover stories under hypnosis. Although the Gestapo were able, under torture, to extract information from a couple of them, they were never able to break their cover story. Why? Because the agents didn't know they were lying; as far as they were concerned, their cover story was the *true* story.'

'Okay,' said Atwell. 'But as you were careful to point out, you've been talking about people who are *susceptible* to hypnosis. Surely there aren't all that many people who are susceptible. I mean, I can't believe I am, for one . . .'

Pohl looked as if he would have liked to take issue with him, but instead he contented himself with answering his question. 'Estimates vary, but the general consensus seems to be that between 70 and 80 per cent of the adult population can be hypnotized. And of these, many can be taken into a state of deep hypnosis in which paralysis, positive and negative hallucinations, regression, amnesia, anaesthesia and the execution of complicated post-hypnotic suggestions can be developed.'

It was game, set and match to Pohl, and he knew it. 'Let me tell you another thing that might surprise you,' he added. 'Although it's quite true that in its clinical application hypnosis is always a co-operative enterprise between doctor and patient, the fact remains that a good subject can be put into a trance in a second and through any number of disguised techniques!'

Pohl had just begun to describe one of the techniques – progressive relaxation – when a bell began to ring. 'That'll be Mr de Souza,' he said, getting to his feet.

After introducing de Souza to Atwell, Pohl sat him down and gave him a drink. 'Well now, we aren't a bit nervous, are we?' he said confidently.

'You may not be, doctor, but I'm in a shocking state!'

Pohl smiled. 'Oh, surely not.' He leaned forward to take hold of de Souza's wrist for a moment. 'Umm . . . your pulse *is* rather high. Did you walk here, by any chance?'

De Souza said he had come by taxi.

'Really?' Pohl sounded faintly concerned. 'Well, just sit back and relax for a moment, there's a good fellow.

'As soon as you feel ready – and there's absolutely no hurry – you and I will go to my consulting room. There, I'll ask you to lie on a couch. I'll be sitting in a chair behind you, and when you feel comfortable I will shine this—' he took a pen-torch out of his pocket and held it up for de Souza to see '—into your eyes—'

'Oh my *God*!' cried de Souza. 'What is it?'

Pohl looked surprised. 'A torch . . .' He switched it on so that de Souza could see it really was a torch. 'Happy?'

De Souza looked anything but happy. 'What happens then?'

'When you are nice and relaxed I'll ask you some questions about what you saw during the evening Miss Tennant left. That's all there is to it! Doesn't sound so bad, does it?'

'It *sounds* all right – I just don't know if I'm going to be any good at it,' said de Souza, miserably. 'I really don't . . .'

'Well, let's see, shall we,' said Pohl, rising to his feet. 'Could I trouble you to stand up for a moment, please.'

He took de Souza's glass from him and guided him out into the middle of the room.

'Now,' he said, 'if you would just stand with your heels together and your eyes closed . . . That's right! Excellent! Now what I'd like you to do is imagine yourself falling . . .'

Pohl moved quietly around so that he was standing beside de Souza, ready to catch him if he lost his balance.

'Forwards or backwards?'

'Forwards would be fine. Just keep your eyes shut and imagine yourself falling . . .'

Pohl waited for almost a minute, but nothing happened.

Then, softly and slowly he said: 'Keep your eyes closed and imagine yourself falling . . . keep your eyes closed and imagine yourself falling . . . gently falling, softly falling, falling, falling . . .'

Suddenly there was a tremendous crash from the direction of the fireplace and de Souza let out a shriek of terror.

Pohl and Fitzpatrick spun around. Staring stupidly up at them from the hearth, where he had fallen flat on his back, was Atwell.

De Souza unlocked the door to his flat, and, followed by Fitzpatrick, swept through into the sitting-room and flung himself down on the settee.

'Oh my God!' he cried. 'What*ever* must you think? Charles, for heaven's sake get me a large pink gin – and something for Mr Fitzpatrick.'

Making it seem like an enormous effort, Charles uncurled himself from in front of the television and crossed to a 1930s cocktail cabinet. 'Well?' he asked Fitzpatrick.

'Not for me – thanks all the same.'

Charles shrugged, as if to say suit yourself, dropped some ice cubes and a dash of bitters into a glass and half-filled it with Gordon's gin.

'Couldn't he do it then?' he asked, thrusting the glass into de Souza's hand as he sauntered back to his chair.

'It really wasn't Mr de Souza's fault.'

'Oh yes it was!' de Souza insisted. 'That poor Dr Pohl tried everything – I felt so embarrassed for him – but he simply *couldn't* get me under! "Non-susceptible," he kept saying. Non-susceptible. *Imagine*!' His mood began to brighten. 'I must say, though, it did have its *funny* side. Fancy poor Mr Atwell falling over like that . . .'

The end credits of the programme Charles had been watching had begun to roll, and he switched off the set. '*What* happened?' he asked, now prepared to take more of an interest in de Souza's adventures.

'You would have *died*, my dear! There was this big butch policeman there, and while the doctor was trying to get *me* to pass out, the policeman – would you believe it – passed out . . . It was simply *dreadful*!'

'But couldn't the shrink have given you a shot of something?'

'Don't! He wanted to, poor lamb, but you know what *I'm* like about needles!'

Charles sighed. 'Well, I never really understood what it was you expected to find out in the first place.'

'A car registration number,' said Fitzpatrick, glancing at his wristwatch. 'Christ, is it really that time?' He got up to go. 'You've been very kind, and I mustn't keep you.'

'The registration number of *which* car?'

'I've told you all about it!' snapped de Souza. 'The one that Mr Fitzpatrick's young lady was taken away in . . .'

'What, the green Fiesta? The one you thought had burglars in it?'

Fitzpatrick sat down again. 'You *saw* it?'

'Yes,' said Charles. 'Madam here got herself into a worse state than usual that evening – thought they'd come to steal her mink.' He snorted. 'Chance would be a fine thing!'

'But you were the first to notice it!' de Souza cried indignantly. 'You pointed it out to me as soon as I was inside the door . . .'

'Only because you'd said that you couldn't get a ticket after six.'

Fitzpatrick frowned. 'What was that about a *ticket*?'

'I went out to get some wheatgerm just after six and I saw this traffic warden putting a parking ticket on the car.' Charles twisted around to look at de Souza. 'It was the old bag you'd had a screaming match with the previous week.'

'Oh, *her*!'

'Now hold it a minute,' said Fitzpatrick. 'Where was the driver when all this was happening?'

Charles shrugged. 'Popped out for a pee or something . . . How should *I* know?'

'Okay, let me get this straight. You saw a traffic warden stick a parking ticket *on the same car that Clair left in later that night*. Is that what you're saying?'

Charles and de Souza glanced at one another, mystified. 'Well, yes . . .' said Charles, lamely.

Fitzpatrick sprang to his feet. 'Can I use your telephone?'

13

When Fitzpatrick arrived back in his office at noon the following day, the vast open-plan newsroom was almost deserted. Most of his fellow reporters were still out on stories, and the copy-tasters and sub-editors who would weld their efforts and those of countless stringers, foreign correspondents, news-agency reporters, and photographers into the next day's paper would not be arriving until after lunch.

The attractive secretary who looked after Fitzpatrick and two other specialist writers was over by the wire machines drinking Coke and chatting with the news editor's secretary. As soon as she caught sight of Fitzpatrick she began threading her way through the rows of carefully regimented desks, passing beneath an enormous sign which read: GET IT RIGHT AND GET IT EARLY.

'How!' she said, saluting him like a Red Indian.

Fitzpatrick grinned. Earlier that morning he had been asked to write a piece about what various people were doing to combat the drought, and he had just returned from seeing a man who was trying to persuade the BBC to broadcast tapes he had made of Mohawk rain-dance music.

'So, meanwhile, what's been happening back at the ranch?' he asked, loosening his tie.

The girl picked up her notebook. 'Do you want the not so good news first or the bad?'

'It's one of *those* days, is it?' He took out his cigarettes and lighter and hung his jacket over the back of his chair. Although he had walked slowly from Temple underground station, and had kept on the shaded side of Fleet Street, the back of his blue shirt was wet with sweat.

The girl nodded. 'Your garage rang to say you're going to need a new gear-box—'

'Jesus! I've only done 25,000 miles!'

'There you go,' she said, with a resigned shrug. 'Anyway, they want you to let them know whether they're to go ahead or not . . .' She turned over a page. 'Now, let's see what other goodies we've got for you.

'The chief hydrogeologist of the Institute of Geological Sciences rang to say that you misquoted him in your story this morning, and will you please call him back as soon as . . .'

Fitzpatrick sat down heavily, burying his head in his hands for a moment.

'Someone called Jo rang to ask if you'll be going to the BP reception tonight . . .'

'In this heat? Call him back and make an excuse, there's a love.'

'It wasn't a him, it was a her – and she sounded very dishy.'

'The answer's still "not tonight".' He dragged over his typewriter and began to roll a sheet of triples into it. Sellotaped to the front of the machine was a notice which read: *Every cigarette you smoke shortens your life by five minutes.*

'By the way, did the guy from the Water Resources Board come back with the figures on desalination?' he asked, lighting a cigarette.

'He did – I was just about to type them.'

'Anything else?'

'Detective Inspector Atwell rang. He wants to know if there's any chance of having lunch with you today. It sounded as if it might be important.'

'Great!' said Fitzpatrick, typing his name and catchline at the head of the sheet. 'Where and when?'

The girl opened his desk diary. 'I said I'd have to let him know. You're supposed to be meeting your friend from the *Sunday Times* in El Vino's at two o'clock . . .'

'Shit! Look, call him and say I'm sorry but something's come up, and can we get together one day next week. Then ask Atwell where he wants to meet. If he says the Cheshire Cheese, tell him it'll be full of American tourists at this time of the year and suggest the Trat – the one in Chancery Lane – at whatever time suits him. Okay?'

'You haven't forgotten that there's an NUJ chapel meeting at one o'clock? I did *tell* you . . .'

'That's just too bad . . .' Fitzpatrick flipped open his shorthand notebook and began typing.

'So much for the international solidarity of the working class!' said the girl, turning to answer a telephone that had begun flashing on the next desk.

'There's more,' she announced, as soon as she had rung off.

Fitzpatrick continued typing. 'Sorry, love, but it'll have to wait.' Then, as an afterthought, he asked: 'Are my ex's through yet?'

'The managing editor wants to see you about them after Conference,' she replied in a sing-song voice.

He looked up. 'That means I haven't got enough money for lunch!'

With a long-suffering expression, the girl opened her desk drawer and reached inside for her handbag.

'How much do you want *this* time?' she asked.

Fitzpatrick arrived to find Atwell sitting at a table on the crowded first floor of the restaurant, sipping a drink and studying the menu intently.

'Reggie, I'm sorry I'm late,' he said, squeezing Atwell's shoulder. 'I was marched in to see the managing editor and it all went on a bit longer than either of us intended.'

'I knew they'd rumble you sooner or later . . .'

Laughing, Fitzpatrick sat down and the waiter who had escorted him to his table broke open a pink napkin and draped it over his lap.

After ordering a Campari and soda, Fitzpatrick tore the top from a packet of breadsticks and began shaking one out. 'So, what's new?'

'Does the name Martha Pierce mean anything to you? Martha Pierce of Miami Beach?'

Fitzpatrick frowned. 'Martha Pierce?' He broke off a piece of breadstick and put it into his mouth. 'No, that's a new one on me . . .'

Atwell looked suprised. 'Clair never mentioned her?'

'No, never. Who is she?'

Like a conjuror producing a rabbit from a hat, Atwell handed him a sheet of paper on which was written Pierce's address and telephone number. 'Only the bird who hired the car that your Clair left in!'

'Christ, that was quick!'

Atwell shrugged as if to say it's easy when you know how. 'First thing this morning I got on to the Central Ticket Office and had them look up all the tickets issued between six and six-thirty on August the 12th.

'Then I got on the blower to Swansea with the registration numbers. Only one – thank God – was a Fiesta, and that belonged to Hertz. Hertz told me the rest.'

Fitzpatrick's drink had arrived, and with it the waiter to take their order.

'If this is on the paper, I'll have the melon and Parma ham and the cold salmon,' said Atwell, choosing two of the most expensive dishes on the menu.

'It is, and I'll have the same,' Fitzpatrick told the waiter. 'Oh, and a bottle of Verdicchio.' He turned back to Atwell. 'So, tell me more.'

'Apparently Pierce picked up the car from Hertz's Mayfair branch early on the morning of August 10th, and returned it on the morning of the 13th.'

'The day after Clair left . . .'

'Right. Listen, do you happen to know if she has an American visa?'

Fitzpatrick nodded. 'She's got a B2 visitor's visa. She got it when she went to New York last year.'

'So there would be nothing to stop her going to Miami if she wanted to?'

'No, nothing.' Fitzpatrick paused to sample the Verdicchio the wine waiter had just uncorked. 'But why would she *want* to go to Miami? She's never been there before; she doesn't know anyone there—'

'She seems to know this Pierce character.'

'I see what you mean . . .' Fitzpatrick looked again at the address Atwell had given him. 'Okay, so what do I do? Ring her and ask what the hell's going on, I suppose . . .'

'I'm not sure. I'm just not sure. On the face of it, calling her is the most sensible thing to do. And yet the old street sense tells me it isn't. I don't suppose your paper has a bureau in Miami, by any chance?'

'Only in New York. Why, what did you have in mind?'

'If there had been one, it might have been worth having someone take a sniff around first. Just to get a feel of the situation, y'know what I mean?'

Fitzpatrick nodded. 'The New York office sends people down occasionally to cover a space-shot or a convention, but as far as I know there's nothing like that coming up in the immediate future . . .'

'H'm.' Atwell thought for a moment. 'It sounds a bit dramatic, but I know a very good private investigator in Miami – a guy called Edward Lippencott. Why don't I call Ed and ask him to take a look around? He owes me a favour, and that way you'd know just what it was you were getting into . . .'

14

'What the hell are *you* doing here?' Quintrell demanded, as he strode into the library of his waterfront mansion on Star Island. 'You know you're never supposed to come *here*!'

'Lee, I'm sorry,' cried Martha Pierce, rushing across to him. 'But we're in trouble! Terrible trouble! I tried to reach you at the theatre, but they said you'd already—'

'Come to the *point*, woman!'

'Lee—' Pierce's bottom lip began to tremble. 'Lee, I've just had a private detective call on me. He's—' She began fumbling in her bag for a handkerchief. 'Oh, Lee - *he's looking for Clair Tennant*!' she cried, and burst into tears.

Quintrell went ashen. 'Oh, my *God*!' he said, his eyes flicking to the window. Outside on a lawn lit by gaily coloured Chinese lanterns, a score of chefs and liveried servants were putting the final touches to an elaborate buffet. 'But I have the Governor and his wife and the entire cast of the London Festival Ballet arriving any minute!'

'Oh, for Christ's *sake*, Lee!' Pierce sobbed into her handkerchief.

Quintrell hurried across to the drinks table and poured a large measure of brandy. 'Here, you'd better have this,' he said, thrusting the glass into her hand. 'Now, tell me exactly what happened.'

After blowing her nose, Pierce took a sip of the brandy. Speaking in short, strangled rushes, she told him about Edward Lippencott's visit and then burst into tears again.

'Oh, *no*!' Quintrell pressed his fingertips against his temples as if suddenly assailed by a blinding headache. 'I'd no *idea* you'd travelled under your real names! The Old Man'll blow his stack!'

Pierce looked up from her handkerchief. 'We've always travelled under our real names!' she protested. 'You know we have! God, Lee—' she sniffed loudly '—if we'd been travelling under false names that time we were picked up by the police in Paris—'

'Okay! *All right*!' Quintrell's headache seemed to have got worse. 'But what'll I tell the Old Man? When he hears about this he'll go *ape*!'

'Is Mr God Almighty Snaith and how he'll react all anyone around here can think about these days?' cried Pierce, her red-rimmed eyes flashing angrily. 'Now for Christ's sake, Lee, will you please do something about cancelling tonight's rationalization?'

Quintrell's mouth sagged open. 'You mean – you mean you haven't *cancelled*?'

'Of course I haven't cancelled!' Pierce replied indignantly. 'You know perfectly well I don't have the authority to cancel a rationalization!'

Quintrell turned to stare stupidly at the carriage clock on the mantelpiece. 'But – but it's almost half-past eleven!' he said in a disbelieving voice. 'Ginzel will already be on his way!'

'Then call Cahill at De Soto Fountain!'

From outside the elegantly furnished room came the sound of cars drawing up on a gravelled driveway. Then, as the clock on the mantelpiece began chiming the half-hour, a string orchestra struck up 'Moonlight and Roses'.

'Oh my God, they're beginning to arrive!'

'Lee, will you *please* ring Cahill?'

'But what good'll that do? Ducasse intends to spoil Tennant before they get to the Fountain!'

'Dammit, Lee, Cahill can call Ginzel on the truck's Citizens' Band radio and tell him the rationalization's been aborted!'

Quintrell took an address book from the inside pocket of his white dinner-jacket and crossed to the telephone. 'This is a foul-up!' he said, beginning to tap out the number of the mobile operator. 'A real *foul-up*! It'll take at least a month to fix Tennant with a false identity. Finding a girl of her age and physique who's died recently isn't going to be easy—' He broke off to give the operator the number of Cahill's car. 'Then there's the business of getting her a *job*, a social *security* card—' He broke off again, this time pressing his hand to his ear. 'Hello? Cahill? It's Quintrell! Look, we've got a problem; *mother's been taken ill!* Have you got that? Okay, now will you let the others know? Yes, I'll hold.'

Covering the mouthpiece, he turned to Pierce. 'The next thing we have to figure out is how we're going to break this to the Old Man. Do I call him, or would it be better—' He held up his hand. '*What*?' he said into the telephone, as his glasses began to steam over. 'But they'll be committed before you reach them! All right, try. For Christ's sake, *try*!'

He banged down the telephone. 'Now it's really hit the fan!' he told Pierce. 'Ginzel's CB radio's out of action!'

15

Fitzpatrick woke up with a start, convinced he had heard Clair calling out to him.

For several seconds he remained bolt upright, waiting for the call to come again. But although the dark, stiflingly hot bedroom still seemed to reverberate with the echo of her cry, the only sound he could now hear was the ticking of the alarm clock.

Covered with sweat and with his heart pounding, he fell back on to the bed.

So far, the idea that she might be in physical danger had not occurred to him. It was true that for a short while after finding the letter from the Institute of Preventive Medicine he had thought she might be ill; but the fears which had suddenly erupted within him were of an altogether more frightening kind.

Although neither he nor Clair had taken such phenomena very seriously, there had been occasions in the past when it had seemed as if they were able to exchange thoughts telepathically. Fitzpatrick found himself remembering an instance earlier that year when Clair, seized by a premonition that something was wrong, had called him late at night in Amsterdam. At the time he had been suffering from what he had thought was nothing more serious than a heavy cold. But at her insistence he had gone to see a doctor the following morning. The doctor had diagnosed viral pneumonia and had sent him straight into hospital.

Fitzpatrick was not a superstitious man, yet he could not rid himself of the chilling feeling that the cry he had heard – or imagined he had heard – was also some kind of premonition.

But what could he possibly do about it? There was no one he could ring, as Clair had done.

He turned to look at the clock. It was 4.30 – 4.30 on the morning of September 9th. Maybe there *was* someone he could ring. In Miami it would still only be 11.30 on the evening of

September 8th – late, but not *too* late for him to ring Lippencott.

That, he decided, was what he would do. He had sent Clair's photograph airmail express, so Lippencott should have made some progress. And if he hadn't, now was as good a time as any to start kicking ass . . .

He switched on the bedside light and turned to the L section in his address book. Then, after lighting a cigarette, he dialled Lippencott's home number.

The phone was answered within seconds by a young woman who seemed to recognize his name. 'No, it isn't too late,' she assured him. 'As a matter of fact, Ed's only just this minute got back. Here he is now . . .'

There was a brief pause and then Lippencott came on the line. 'Mr Fitzpatrick? Good to hear from you!' The voice was warm and friendly, the accent Standard Network English. 'Too late? Hell, no! We run a 24-hour service and the second cup of coffee's free! Tell me, how's Reggie?'

'He's fine. He sends his best wishes.'

'I haven't seen him in a long time – in fact not since I was over in Brighton the year before last to attend a World Association of Detectives' Convention. He sure is one helluva nice guy . . .

'Say, it's kinda spooky you calling me up like this,' Lippencott continued. 'You know who I've just come from seeing? Martha Pierce! How about that?'

'You *have*?'

'Don't get too excited,' Lippencott warned. 'I'm not sure it's gotten us very far, except in a negative sense.

'Say, do you happen to know Miami at all well?'

'I've never been there.'

'Well, this Pierce dame lives in a pretty ritzy apartment in what I guess would be Miami Beach's equivalent of Mayfair.

'She's in her late forties and beginning to show her mileage, and she works as some kind of executive secretary for a local big-shot doctor. An Englishman, as a matter of fact.

'I should explain that before going to see her I had one of my people check out whether anyone answering Miss Tennant's description had been seen entering or leaving the Pierce residence. The answer was no. I also checked to see if there were any yellow sheets on Pierce. Again, the answer was no.

'So, I figured I'd nothing to lose by going along and laying it on the line for her.

'I was expecting her to give me a real bad time, but she didn't. She doesn't deny she was in London last month, or that she hired a Fiesta from Hertz while she was over there. But what she does insist is that she's never even *heard* of Miss Tennant, let alone ever visited her.'

'But that's crazy!' said Fitzpatrick. 'If she didn't visit her, how would we have been able to trace her?'

'Her story is that she'd gone to Chelsea to do some shopping, and had stayed over to have dinner with friends in a King's Road restaurant.'

'But why park in Tite Street? I don't know if you realize it, but Tite Street's a good ten minutes' walk away from the King's Road.'

'That's right – I'd checked it out on a street map before going to see her. When I put this to her, she said that she wasn't all that familiar with the district, and that Tite Street was the nearest place she could find in which to park. Does that make any kind of sense to you?'

'I suppose it's just about possible,' Fitzpatrick conceded. 'But how does she explain the fact that she was seen driving off with Clair and a man carrying Clair's suitcases?'

'Again, she's got what sounds like a plausible story. She says she gave the couple with whom she'd had dinner a lift home and that it was *them* your eyeball saw getting into the car—'

'But what about the man with the suitcases? Who goes out to dinner carrying *suitcases*?'

'According to Pierce they weren't suitcases, they were cardboard boxes with handles.'

'They were *what*?'

'Cardboard boxes with handles. But this is something maybe you could check out at your end. She says she bought some clothes in the King's Road branch of a shop called Jaeger – is that how you pronounce it?'

'Jaeger – that's right . . .'

'Anyway, Jaeger apparently packed the clothes in two grey

cardboard boxes with some kind of plastic handle. Although they weren't particularly heavy, the guy she was with – or so she says – insisted on carrying them from the restaurant to the car.'

'Does she still have the boxes?'

'No, she doesn't. But she was able to produce a coat and a trouser suit with Jaeger labels . . .'

'You know, now that I think about it,' said Fitzpatrick, sheepishly, 'Jaeger *do* use that kind of box. I bought a suit from them last month and they packed it in a grey box with a plastic handle . . .'

'As I understand it, your witness was in an apartment on the second floor of a block next door, right?'

'That's right.'

'And all the comings and goings he reported took place after dark?'

'It would certainly have been dark by the time they left.'

'Say, tell me one thing, Mr Fitzpatrick: just *how* reliable is this guy of yours? Because it's beginning to look as if he made a number of faulty observations from which he drew incorrect inferences. Does that sound possible to you?'

'I'm afraid it sounds *entirely* possible!'

16

In fact, there was nothing at all wrong with Ginzel's CB radio. Less than ten minutes before Cahill had begun trying to raise him, Ginzel's partner – a big, sleepy-eyed negro named Angelo – had exchanged greetings with another trucker who had called to warn them that 'Smokey Bears were handing out green stamps on the superslab near the Brickell Avenue turnoff'.

It was then that Ginzel had first noticed a curious noise coming from the engine of the rig he was driving. 'What the fuck do you suppose that is?' he had asked.

Angelo had turned down the CB radio to listen with him. 'Gee, it sounds kinda like you're having trouble with the transmission.'

Alarmed at the prospect of a breakdown, Ginzel had stopped and, together with Angelo, had spent several minutes fruitlessly searching for the cause of the noise.

Still worried, they had climbed back into the cab and set off again – but with all thoughts of the still silent CB radio now absent from their minds.

Ducasse looked up from arranging surgical instruments on a non-slip pad as Angelo's voice began blaring from the speaker mounted on the inside front bulkhead of the rig: *'Listen you guys, we're still getting a racket from the engine. Something's wrong somewhere. I guess it wouldn't be a bad idea if you'd run a check on all your power-operated equipment, just in case. Okay?'*

Ducasse glanced at his watch and swore. With only fifteen minutes to go to zero hour, this was no time to be developing mechanical trouble.

Careful not to lose his footing in the swaying truck, he squeezed past the litter on which Clair Tennant was lying, and made his way across to the rig's master control console. 'Right,' he said to his two rubber-aproned assistants, 'we'd better take it from the top, and in sequence.'

The first of the array of switches Ducasse flicked caused a

false bulkhead at the rear of the rig to part down the middle. Slowly, the two halves began to rotate about their axes, bringing into view rows of linen-wrapped carcasses of meat. As soon as the two sections of false bulkhead were parallel with one another they began to slide in opposite directions, finally locking neatly into place on either side of the rig.

Ducasse flicked another switch, sending the ramps carrying the wrecked Volkswagen rolling gently forward between the sides of meat to stop just short of the rear doors.

'Well, that all seems to be okay,' he said. 'Now let's run a check on the trauma equipment.'

He turned back to the console and pulled a lever. This time, the specially adapted dentist's chair began to slide backwards along a track running from the front bulkhead to a point six inches short of the Volkswagen's rear fender. At the opposite end of the track and directly in line with the chair was a section cut from the upper edge of a Volkswagen's windshield, a portion of dashboard, a steering wheel and a set of foot pedals. Sticking out between the upper edge of the windshield and the dashboard were a number of ugly-looking slivers of glass.

As soon as the chair had reached the end of the track, red warning lights began flashing at either end of the rig.

'Everyone clear?' asked Ducasse as he reached for another of the switches. 'Right – here goes . . .'

With an enormous whummp, a blast of compressed air sent the chair rocketing forward along the track until it came to a quivering stop exactly seven-and-a-quarter inches short of the steering wheel.

'Fine,' said Ducasse, looking again at his watch. 'We should be almost there by now, so while we're waiting for the pressure to build up again, let's get Tennant strapped into position.'

The passenger officer in the black-and-yellow highway patrol car that was cruising east along the South Dixie Highway suddenly turned.

'Hey, Sarge,' he said, staring back through the rear window, 'isn't that the meat wagon someone was trying to raise a while back?'

His partner glanced up at the driving mirror. 'If it is, he's sure as hell pushing it some.'

'How do you feel about going after him?'

The sergeant thought about it for a moment. So far it had been a quiet night and they were coming up to an emergency vehicle gap in the central reservation. 'I guess maybe we'd better had.'

The sergeant set his turn-signal indicator flashing, eased over into the high-speed lane and braked, then made a grinding U-turn out on to the east-west section of the highway.

After overtaking several other vehicles, he fell in behind the big ten-wheeled refrigeration truck and began to pace it. 'Like I thought,' he growled, 'the sonuvabitch is way over the limit! Okay, let's find out what gives . . .'

The patrolman reached for the public-address microphone and put it to his lips. 'Police!' he said, speaking slowly and distinctly. 'Check your mirror, reduce speed gradually, pull over and stop!'

Immediately, the truck's braking lights glowed red. Then, with its turn-indicator flashing, it began to move over towards the side of the road, losing speed rapidly.

As the two vehicles came to a standstill, the police officers unfastened their seat belts, put on their straw Stetsons and stepped out on to the oil-stained highway.

By the time the sergeant had made his unhurried way over to the door of the cab, Ginzel had wound down the window. 'Something the matter, doc?' he asked.

'Switch off your engine and break out your ID.'

Ginzel wiped his sweating hands on his white coverall, dug into a pocket for his papers and passed them down to the sergeant.

'Okay,' he said, after satisfying himself that they were in order. 'Now supposing you tell me how come you were doing ten miles an hour over the limit, huh?'

Ginzel slapped the steering wheel with the flat of his hand. 'Goddamit!' he said, turning to Angelo. 'You know what? That fuckin' speedo's on the blink again!'

The sergeant shook his head, as if saddened to think that

Ginzel hadn't been able to come up with a better excuse. 'And what about your CB radio? I suppose that's on the blink, too . . .'

Ginzel gave him a puzzled look, then leaned forward and began fiddling with the knobs of the radio. Suddenly the cab was filled with a blast of chatter. '*You gotta copy on me?*' someone was asking, painfully loud. '*A big ten-four!*' came the reply. '*What's your ten-twenty, Brake One Eight?*'

Ginzel snapped back the volume, and, after giving Angelo a dirty look, turned again to the sergeant. By now he had been rejoined by the patrolman, who had been walking around the truck – flashlight in hand – checking its tyres and bodywork.

'Everything okay back there?' asked the sergeant.

The patrolman nodded. 'Want me to look at the controls?'

The sergeant began to say something, but his words were swallowed up by the roar of a passing gasolene tanker. He turned back to Ginzel, and as soon as he could be heard, said: 'This time I'm going to let you off without a citation. But only because we've just intercepted a message from your dispatcher calling you back to the depot.'

'Back to the depot? Why, what's up?'

'Your mother's been taken ill.'

Ginzel looked suitably shocked. 'Jesus!' he said, running his hand through his hair.

'Where's your depot?'

'Over near the Orange Bowl . . .'

'Right,' said the sergeant, turning to point out a spot about a quarter of a mile ahead. 'I'm going to let you make a U-turn through the emergency vehicle gap. Okay? Drive over and wait for me there.

'And listen, buddy, take it easy, huh?' he added, as his partner began to make his way back to the patrol car. 'Remember, the life you save may be your own.'

The sergeant stepped back from the cab, and, as soon as the road behind was clear, waved the rig away.

As the rig began to roll, the three men hidden inside lowered the hammers on their Colt .45s and reholstered them.

The red warning lights were flashing, and the chair they had tested less than ten minutes earlier was back in its firing position. Now, however, it was occupied by Clair Tennant.

'Okay, unstrap her,' Ducasse told his assistants. 'The party's over for tonight.'

17

Fitzpatrick had promised de Souza that he would call the moment there was any news. So, as soon as he had showered and made himself a cup of coffee, he rang to recount the story he had been told by Lippencott four hours earlier.

De Souza was outraged. 'But it *was* Miss Tennant!' he insisted. 'I know it was. She was wearing a patterned headscarf tied at the back and one of those sweet little trouser suits that are all the rage at the moment.

'And as for the Pierce woman saying she was carrying cardboard boxes – well, *really*! – that's absolute nonsense! They were *suitcases*. And they were brown, not grey. Brown matching suitcases with straps around them.

'Whatever else might be beginning to flag,' he added, 'my eyesight's as good as it's ever been!'

Fitzpatrick arrived at his office just before the start of the 10.30 features conference. With still some weeks to go before the beginning of the autumn advertising bonanza, the following day's paper was to be a thin one, with the feature pages given over mainly to gardening, women's interest articles and previews of the weekend television programmes.

As often happened on a Friday, Fitzpatrick came out of the conference without having offered a story or been assigned one. It was his secretary's day off and he had already been through that day's papers at home, so, after getting himself a cup of the almost undrinkable canteen coffee, he began looking for something to read.

A search of nearby desks turned up *Sports Illustrated*, *Newsweek* and *Time*. He returned to his seat, swung his feet up on to the scarred metal desk top and began leafing through *Time*.

But his mind was not really on it; de Souza's insistence that it was Clair he had seen leaving, and, more disturbing still, the fact of his being able to describe her luggage so accurately, had rekindled all of Fitzpatrick's earlier fears.

Soon, he was wondering whether he oughtn't to take some

of the holiday that was due to him and go to Miami to nose around for himself.

Laying aside *Time*, he began making a rough estimate of what such a trip would cost. With the pound still badly undervalued against the dollar, however, he soon realized that making the 8,800-mile round trip under his own steam was out of the question.

He screwed up the paper on which he had made his calculations, tossed it into a waste-bin and once more picked up *Time*.

The magazine fell open at a page with a picture of Frank Mancini emerging from the door of an aircraft, his hands clasped above his head in a boxer's salute. Next to it was a picture of the President's plaid-shirted brother, a can of beer in one hand and a placard reading *Protect your right to bear arms* in the other. Below the headline *Fight to Control Firearms*, was the subhead *With friends like these, who needs enemies.*

Fitzpatrick began reading the accompanying story: *As the controversy over the Firearms Control Bill* (Time, *Aug 1*) *begins to heat up, the President finds himself with an unlikely enemy, and an even more unlikely ally. Opposing the Bill is the President's brother; defending it, big-game hunter and skin-mag publisher Frank ('This is the first thing they've come up with in seven years that makes any kind of sense') Mancini.*

Fitzpatrick's interest began to wander. But, just as he was about to turn the page, his eye was caught by a paragraph two-thirds of the way down the first column: *Currently in a fashion-able Miami Beach clinic awaiting a heart transplant, Mancini defended his dramatic turnabout on the issue of gun control by saying—*

Wait a minute! thought Fitzpatrick, turning to the cover to make sure he wasn't reading an out-of-date issue. If Mancini's in Miami, perhaps I could get the paper to send me?

As a specialist writer, Fitzpatrick liked to think of himself as being his own master. In fact he had two – the news editor and the features editor. He immediately dismissed the idea of trying to persuade the news editor to send him. As a news story, Mancini's heart transplant wasn't worth more than a paragraph, and then only in the paper's America column. For that matter, it wasn't all that great a feature subject – Mancini's was not exactly a household name, or at least not in Britain. However, it was a story about the sufferings of the rich (the favourite topic, or so it is believed in Fleet Street, of readers of mass-circulation newspapers), and he could use it as a peg on which to hang a couple of hundred words about the transplantation situation in Britain.

Although he knew it wasn't going to be an easy deal to swing, he set out for the features editor's office determined to try his damnedest.

'Hey, have you seen that Frank Mancini's having a heart transplant?' Fitzpatrick began, trying to make it sound like the greatest story since the Crucifixion.

But the features editor – a thin, pale young man with a Mancunian accent – was used to the hard sell. 'It's the first time anyone's suggested he had a heart to transplant,' he said, looking up from the overnight page proofs he was busily re-scheming. 'Anyway, what about it?'

Fitzpatrick handed him the magazine. 'There,' he said, pointing to the story. 'Christ, he'd make a great subject for an interview, specially with the transplant angle.'

The features editor began to read. 'But it says here that he's in a clinic in Miami!' he exclaimed. 'If you're expecting me to send you to *Miami*, you want your bumps feeling!'

Swivelling round on his stool, he plucked a newspaper clip off a spike on his desk and thrust it at Fitzpatrick. 'If you're looking for something to do, follow that up . . .'

'I did it last month. It was pulled after the first edition . . .' Fitzpatrick returned the cutting. 'Now listen,' he continued. 'Supposing I can discover the donor's name? Talk to his wife and children, his parents . . . Better still, supposing the donor turns out to be a *woman*. How about that? The king of the male chauvinist pigs with a woman's heart!'

The features editor pushed up his glasses and began rubbing his red-rimmed eyes. 'It's a nice idea,' he replied, 'but the answer's still no. Quite apart from the fact it probably won't *be* a woman, we're supposed to be making a 15 per cent cut in expenditure. And anyway, they'd never tell you the donor's name. They never do.'

'We know the name of Louis Washkansky's donor – it was Denise Darvall . . .'

'We only know that because it was the *first* heart transplant,' protested the features editor. 'Things have changed a lot since then.'

Fitzpatrick decided the time had come to try another tack. 'You know, there's a good piece to be done about the Firearms Control Bill.'

The features editor mimed the action of pulling a lavatory chain. 'It's been done to death.'

'Wait a minute – nobody's yet written a piece about the different *types* of weapon that are—'

'It's not for us – not until the Bill gets thrown out on its arse.'

Fitzpatrick had shot his bolt. 'All right, I'll level with you,' he said. 'I need a couple of days in Miami for personal reasons.'

'You and me, too! Listen, chuck, my wife says that if I even as much as *mention* taking her and the kids to Bognor again next year, she'll walk out on me!'

'I'm not going to Miami for a *holiday*—'

'You're not going to Miami, period! Or at least you're not going on *my* foreign budget.'

Fitzpatrick turned and walked towards the door. But the features editor had begun to soften. 'Just how important *is* it for you to go to Miami?' he called after him.

'It's important. Very important, as a matter of fact.'

'Well, why didn't you say so in the first place, you daft ha'p'orth.

'Okay, so what makes you think you're going to be able to get to Mancini? He's in the business of publishing interviews, not giving 'em.'

'I've already called his New York office,' Fitzpatrick lied. 'It's as good as fixed.'

The features editor thought it over for a moment. 'Would you be prepared to do a piece about Miami Beach for the New Year's travel supplement while you're out there?'

'If it gets me to Miami, I'd write a piece about how many times a day I have to go to the loo!'

18

'In ten minutes we will be landing at Miami International Airport,' said the stewardess. 'Would you now please extinguish your cigarettes and fasten your seatbelts.'

Fitzpatrick gathered together the books and brochures he had picked up just before leaving London and began bundling them into his briefcase. Then, after stowing the folding table on which he had been working, he wound his watch back five hours to the local time of 8.58 p.m., fastened his seatbelt and began reading through his notes.

In order to have as much time as possible to look for Clair, he had roughed out his article for the New Year's travel supplement. The tone of the piece, he had decided, would be cynical. Not so cynical that it would send the newspaper's advertising director rushing to the features editor hinting darkly at the business they would lose if the offending passages were not removed, but cynical enough for it to be apparent that the author was a journalist and not a writer of puffs. He had begun by explaining that Miami and Miami Beach were two separate cities; Miami being the commercial and industrial centre of Florida, and Miami Beach – a long narrow island linked to the mainland by a number of causeways – the recreational centre.

This was followed by a couple of paragraphs of history. Once a sleepy fishing village of less than three hundred people, Miami had been opened up by the Florida East Coast Railway in 1896. At first, nobody had bothered much about the handful of alligator and mosquito-infested islands lying out in Biscayne Bay. Not, that is, until 1910, when a millionaire from Indiana named Carl Fisher had brought in men, machinery and elephants to begin the long, arduous task of transforming the sand spits, the mangrove swamps and the palmetto jungles into beaches and tropical gardens.

He had gone on to describe Miami Beach as it is today – an island without industries, airport, railroad, buses or cemetery, and where, during the winter season, tourists outnumber residents thirty to one. An island with little else except shops,

114

apartment houses and hotels. Hotels packed so tightly together that from the island's main thoroughfare, Collins Avenue, it is almost impossible to see the ocean (ice-palaces, ornate beyond belief, he'd described them as, where the air-conditioning is kept at a chilling 68 degrees so that the women can wear mink with their diamonds).

If he found himself with any time to spare he thought he might take a look at Seaquarium, but the rest – museums, zoos, parks, golf courses and racetracks – he would write about from material he intended to pick up from the Miami Beach tourist office and Chamber of Commerce.

Relieved to have broken the back of a boring job, he put away his draft and turned to look out of the window. Just coming into view beyond the leading edge of the starboard wing was what looked like a jewelled necklace flung casually down on a black velvet cloth – the islands of Key Biscayne, Virginia Key, Fisher Island and Miami Beach.

Linking the islands to a flat, even more dazzlingly bejewelled mainland were several long, narrow ribbons of slowly moving red and white lights he recognized as traffic crossing the Rickenbacker, MacArthur and Julia Tuttle causeways.

The islands slipped out of sight behind the wing and soon he was looking down on the grid of brilliantly lit streets and avenues of metropolitan Miami.

Suddenly he felt himself becoming depressed. Even if Clair was somewhere below – and from what he had read, Miami seemed like the last place on earth for her to go – how in the name of God was he ever to find her? By comparison with the task he had set himself, finding a needle in a haystack would have been child's play.

He began to fill out his customs declaration card. By the time he had finished and put on his shoes, the jumbo had been brought around to the final approach, and had begun to flare out level with the runway.

They were now sinking fast, and as Fitzpatrick felt the wheels bump down he turned to the window again, hoping for a glimpse of the Florida burrowing owls that live in the wildlife sanctuary between the runways. Although in his article he had written about the owls being everywhere, he saw none.

After clearing immigration and customs, Fitzpatrick picked up his suitcase and typewriter and made his way over to the arrivals gate.

Although he hadn't expected Lippencott to look like Humphrey Bogart in *The Maltese Falcon*, the man carrying a copy of Gibbon's *Decline and Fall* (Lippencott's way of identifying himself to Fitzpatrick) was not at all what he had expected. He was well over six feet tall, with a broad, friendly face, thick brown hair and a neatly trimmed beard, and he was wearing tinted aviator glasses, jeans and an unzipped black leather jacket with diagonal pockets. Hanging down in front of his Jethro Tull T-shirt was a huge silver medallion.

Fitzpatrick walked up to him, quite prepared to discover that someone else was using the same book for the same purpose. 'Ed? Ed Lippencott?'

'Mike? Hi there! Welcome to Miami!'

As soon as the preliminaries were over, Lippencott picked up Fitzpatrick's suitcase and they began to make their way across the busy concourse. 'So, how long are you planning to stay?'

'A week at the most. I managed to persuade the paper to let me do a piece about Frank Mancini.'

'I'd heard he was in town. What's that all about?'

'The story is he's having a heart transplant,' Fitzpatrick replied, as a voice boomed out over the public-address system, announcing the arrival of another flight.

Lippencott frowned. 'A hair transplant?'

'A *heart* transplant! Or at least I hope it is; if it's a hair transplant I'm in bad trouble. Although his press office won't actually confirm the heart transplant story, they haven't denied it – which usually means it's true.'

The automatic doors parted and they stepped out on to the sidewalk. To the west, the sky still held the scarlet afterglow of a subtropical sunset, and the air was warm and thick as blood.

'Y'know, I damned nearly took an infarction myself when I heard he was getting behind the Firearms Control Bill,' said Lippencott, as they threaded their way through the slowly moving line of cars and taxis and airport buses. 'And I kid you not, he really *is* getting behind it. Full page ads in all his papers,

TV and radio commercials – the lot. Hell, he's even begun bussing guys in to picket their senators and congressmen!'

He paused to grind out the stub of the panatella he had been smoking. 'It's all very commendable, except I'd like someone to ask him why – if he's suddenly so worried – he doesn't do something about cutting back on the amount of violence that's pumped out by his TV stations every goddamned night. Do you know that most kids over here see something like thirty-five thousand killings on TV by the time they've grown up? Thirty-five *thousand*, man! And we're surprised when we hear that crimes of violence have become a growth industry!'

'He'd probably say he's already cut it back from what it was,' replied Fitzpatrick. 'However, it's a good question and I'll add it to my list.'

Lippencott led him into a vast, brilliantly lit parking lot. 'By the way, which hospital is he at?'

'Something called the Snaith Clinic.'

'I'll be damned! That's where Martha Pierce works. Didn't I tell you?'

'I don't think so . . . Tell me something, Ed, do you happen to know if this is the *same* Snaith who all the fuss was about a couple of years ago? The one who was involved in a project for growing spare parts for transplantation?'

'That's the guy.'

Fitzpatrick looked impressed.

'Why, d'you know him?'

'I know *about* him. He's supposed to be quite an operator. Difficult, but impressive. In fact before everything went sour on him, he was being talked of as Nobel Prize material.'

'So what's he doing running a clinic for the blue-rinse set in Miami?'

Fitzpatrick shrugged. 'Copping out, I guess . . .'

'That and making a lot of bread!'

Lippencott walked up to a multi-coloured Chrysler van fitted with gleaming mag wheels, unlocked the rear doors and began stowing the luggage. Inside, Fitzpatrick caught a glimpse of black quilted walls, a rosewood table flanked by a pair of banquettes covered in white fur fabric, and, standing next to a fully stocked bar, what looked like a microwave oven.

117

Surprisingly for such a laid-back vehicle, the rear fender was covered with Law and Order stickers, one of which read: 'If you don't like cops, the next time you're in trouble call a hippie.'

'So, when do you get to see Pierce?' Lippencott asked, as he relocked the doors.

'I still don't know. I've tried calling her, but she's always been out. Tomorrow morning, I hope.'

'If de Souza's right, and it was Clair he saw getting into Pierce's automobile – well, I just don't get it. Why build an alibi like we were trying to pin a murder rap on her? Jesus, all she needed to say was yes, I know her, and yes, she's over here but everything's fine, I'll tell her you called, goodbye!'

Lippencott went around and unlocked the passenger door. 'Anyway, take it easy,' he said, scooping up a copy of *Ramparts*. 'It mightn't look like it, but Miami's a pretty tough town.'

'Miami a tough town?' Fitzpatrick climbed into the van.

'Hell, yes!' Lippencott got in beside him, switched on the headlights and the ignition, and then hit the start button on the stereo cassette player. Fitzpatrick braced himself, expecting the sledge-hammer beat of a rock band. Instead, the van filled with the sparkling cascade of strings from the opening of Mozart's 'Haffner' Symphony. 'Miami used to be the winter capital of the National Crime Syndicate,' Lippencott explained. 'At one time we had 'em all here: Jake and Meyer Lansky, Joe Adonis, Vincent Alo, Phil "the Stick" Kovolick . . . Listen, Al *Capone* died out on an island in Biscayne Bay, for chrissake!

'Kefauver did a lot to help clean things up, but then, when Castro took over from Batista back in the late '50s, the guys who'd been running the rackets in Cuba simply shut up shop and returned to Florida.

'Today, Miami's what I guess you could call the cocaine capital of the world. In this town, hustling coke's an eight-*billion*-dollars-a-year business . . .'

Lippencott revved the engine and began to pull away. 'So, my friend, tread softly,' he said. 'And if you think you're getting into something you can't handle, call me. I may not be able to handle it *either*, but at least you'll have company!'

Because of the time difference, Fitzpatrick woke at dawn the following morning. He was staying at one of the less expensive hotels at the southern end of Miami Beach, and, after getting himself coffee from a vending machine, went for a walk along an Ocean Front Park that was deserted except for a couple jogging at the water's edge.

It was 7.45 when he got back to his hotel – 12.45 London time. Determined to avoid having his body chemistry upset by the time change, he rang room service and ordered what for him would be lunch – orange juice, scrambled eggs and bacon and coffee.

As soon as he had finished, he rolled the trolley out into the corridor and hung a DO NOT DISTURB notice on the door handle. Back in his room, he took a portable tape-recorder out of his suitcase and carried it across to the telephone. Then, after making sure he had attached the microphone to the right spot on the telephone cradle by recording a portion of Dial-a-Prayer, he asked the operator to call Martha Pierce's number.

The telephone was answered by what sounded like an elderly coloured woman.

'May I speak to Miss Pierce, please?'

'Ah donno if she's in,' the woman replied grumpily. 'Who wants her?'

'Michael Fitzpatrick.'

The phone at the other end was laid down, none too gently, and he heard her go stomping off, muttering to herself.

After what seemed like several minutes, the woman returned. 'Mrs Pierce ain't here.'

'Could you give me a number where I can reach her?'

'Sorry, mister. Ah's jest the cleanin' woman.'

Fitzpatrick forced a smile back into his voice. 'Oh well, never mind. Perhaps I could speak to Miss Tennant instead?'

'Who?'

'Clair Tennant. I understood she was staying with Mrs Pierce.'

'Ain't nobody of that name heah.'

'Are you sure? Miss Tennant's English, tall and with—'

'Sure ah's sure! Say, where're you callin' from?'

Fitzpatrick gave her the name of his hotel and the telephone number. 'Would you please ask Mrs Pierce to ring me when she returns.'

The woman muttered something he didn't catch, and then, as he was thanking her for her help, she hung up on him.

'Shit!' he said out loud; then asked the operator to call the Snaith Clinic. But Pierce wasn't there either, nor was she expected.

He lit a cigarette and considered what he should do next. There didn't seem much point in door-stepping her apartment; he didn't know what she looked like, and it was pretty obvious that Clair wasn't staying with her. He glanced at his watch: it was 8.45. What he'd do, he decided, was call Mancini's press office at 9.00, confirm the time and place for the interview, then spend a couple of hours at Seaquarium. The chances were that Pierce wouldn't return his call until the afternoon, and if he left within the next half-hour he would be back again by noon.

In fact, it was nearly 10.30 before he was able to leave.

When Mancini had telexed him in London agreeing to be interviewed, he had attached no conditions. However, on calling the press office, Fitzpatrick had been told that not only would he have to provide them with a list of questions, but that he was also expected to submit his copy for Mancini's approval before publication.

After a great deal of argument a compromise had been reached: the press office would drop its demand for a list of questions providing Fitzpatrick promised to stay away from the subject of Mancini's previous marriages. And providing he allowed them to check his copy for what they called 'errors of fact but not opinion', they would not insist on the right of approval before publication.

But then, when the horse trading was finally over, they had sprung another surprise on him: Mancini had left Miami for the clinic in the Bahamas. However, before Fitzpatrick had had a chance to protest, he'd been told that a helicopter had been laid on to fly him to and from the island in four days' time.

Fitzpatrick gathered up his papers, put on his jacket and tie, and took the elevator to the lobby.

While waiting to hand in his key at the reception desk, he began studying the street map he was carrying. He saw that as the crow flies Seaquarium was only about five miles from the hotel. Yet, according to the map, getting there would involve him in a fifteen-mile, U-shaped journey through downtown Miami.

As soon as the desk clerk was free, he asked him whether this really was so.

'I'm afraid it is, Mr Fitzpatrick,' he replied. 'There are no bridges between here and Virginia Key. What you have to do is this . . .'

19

Fitzpatrick arrived at the entrance to the Miami Seaquarium at a little before 11.15. The 35-minute drive had taken him on to the mainland via the MacArthur Causeway, south along Biscayne Boulevard past the tropical gardens of Bayfront Park, on to Brickell Avenue (where they had been held up for ten minutes by marchers demanding tougher law enforcement) and from there back again across Biscayne Bay, this time by way of the Rickenbacket Causeway.

After buying a ticket and a guide book, he began walking down a long tree-lined mall with a flower-bed in the middle. With barely enough breeze to stir the flags on top of the entrance hall ahead of him, it was now stupefyingly hot and humid.

He quickened his pace, passed between a pair of stone dolphins and entered the dark, air-conditioned foyer.

After cooling off in front of the viewing windows of what his guide book called the 'Main Seaquarium' – an 80-foot-wide, 16-foot-deep tank containing bottlenose dolphins, sea turtles, moray eels and giant sea bass – he moved on to a smaller tank filled with brilliantly coloured reef fish.

From the reef tank he went outside again, crossed under the monorail, and, after spending ten minutes watching a couple of huge, black-and-white killer whales at play, began to make his way towards a gold geodesic dome he could see protruding through the trees on the opposite side of the grounds.

After stopping for a drink at the cafeteria, he set out again, but had not got far when he heard someone with what sounded like a Cuban accent call his name. He turned and saw two heavily built men hurrying towards him.

The taller and older-looking man grinned, revealing a pair of gold-capped eye-teeth. 'Ah!' he said triumphantly. 'Meester Fitzpatrick. So, we've found you at last!'

The man took off his grey straw hat and wiped the sweat from his brow with the back of one of his enormous hands.

'Sure ees a hot one!' he said, beginning to fan himself with his hat. 'My name's Morales, and thees gentl'man—' he paused to nod at his companion, a balding, baby-faced man with side-burns and a thin, black moustache '—thees gentl'man's Meester Sanchez.' Morales paused again, this time to wipe away a drop of sweat from the end of his bulbous, slightly pock-marked nose. 'We're from Department of Immigration.'

'Mr Fitzpatrick, do you happen to have your passport with you?' asked Sanchez. His voice was deeper, and less heavily accented than that of Morales.

'My passport?' Fitzpatrick took off his sunglasses and looked from one man to the other. 'No, I don't. I left it in my hotel room. Why, what's the problem?'

Morales shook his head sadly. 'Sorry to have to tell you thees, but your room's been burglarized.'

'It can't have been!' Fitzpatrick exclaimed. 'I haven't been gone from it for more than an hour or so . . .

'And anyway,' he added, suddenly suspicious, 'how did you know where to find me?'

'We were told by the desk clerk,' Sanchez explained. 'They don't seem to have taken much, which is why we think it was probably your passport they were after. Passports fetch a lot of money in this town.'

'Oh Christ!' said Fitzpatrick, running his fingers through his hair. 'That's *all* I need . . .'

Morales shrugged as if to say: these things happen. 'Next time eet mightn't be a bad idea eef you were to maybe leave eet in the hotel safe, y'know what I mean?'

Fitzpatrick nodded. 'And I suppose they've taken my type-writer too, have they? And my tape-recorder?'

'Tape-recorder?' Morales's small, closely set eyes suddenly looked troubled. 'I saw no tape-recorder.' He turned to San-chez. 'You see a tape-recorder?'

Sanchez shook his head emphatically. 'No. There was no tape-recorder.' He glanced at his watch. 'In fact what we'd like you to do is come back to the hotel with us so that we can make out a list of just what *has* been stolen. Would you mind doing that?'

Morales put on his hat and got ready to leave. 'Eet won't take long,' he explained. 'And we'll bring you back here again afterwards.'

'Of course,' said Fitzpatrick. But as the three of them began to move towards the exit, he suddenly hesitated. 'I suppose I'd better ask to see your warrant cards . . .'

The Cubans exchanged bewildered glances.

'Your IDs . . .'

'Ah!' Morales smiled, revealing his gold eye-teeth again. 'But of course!' he said affably. 'We'll show 'em you in automobile.'

Thoughts of the soaring crime rate in America suddenly flashed into Fitzpatrick's mind. 'If it's okay with you, I'd rather see them now . . .'

Morale's smile flickered and died. 'When we're in automobile,' he said, reaching out for Fitzpatrick's elbow. 'Come . . .'

'Sorry, but until I've seen your IDs I'm not going anywhere.'

Sanchez muttered something in Spanish, and Morales dug into his hip pocket and produced a black crocodile-skin billfold. As he did so, his jacket gaped open just enough to reveal that he was wearing a shoulder holster containing an automatic.

'Satisfied?' he asked, giving Fitzpatrick a quick glimpse of what he realized was nothing more than an American driving licence.

It had already occurred to him that even if his room had been broken into, it was unlikely that anyone would have come looking for him, much less immigration officers. Who, then, were these men, and what did they want with him? If it had been a situation in a movie, he knew what he would have done: he would have gone with them, found out what it was all about and then jumped them. Either that or jumped them now. If there had been only one man he might have been tempted, but not with two. To have taken on two heavily built, armed men would have been madness.

He looked anxiously around, hoping that one of Sea-quarium's pith-helmeted guards was near. Although he had noticed several earlier, now he could see only visitors. There was nothing for it but to get away, and get away fast.

As Morales put his billfold back into his pocket, Fitzpatrick spun around and began running as fast as his legs would carry him. '*Tu madre!*' he heard one of the men cry.

Ahead, people were crossing a bridge which looked as if it might have been a rear exit from Seaquarium. As he got closer, he realized that it was one of several leading only to a small tree-covered island surrounded by a moat. However, with the Cubans sounding as if they were catching up with him fast, there was nothing he could do but to keep going.

Once on the island, he turned left. As he did so he saw that the Cubans had parted company. While Morales was elbowing his way through the crowds pouring over the bridge he had just crossed, Sanchez was racing towards the next bridge along.

With his lungs almost bursting, Fitzpatrick skidded to a halt, wondering what the hell to do next.

Only a few feet away he noticed that the moat was crossed by what appeared to be a feeding gantry – two orange-coloured girders supporting a platform surrounded by a handrail on which was hanging a pair of life-belts.

Pushing his way through the crowd lining the railings, he took a closer look. If he used the gantry to get back to the mainland, he would have to walk the first ten feet on one of the narrow girders. Although it was not a prospect he relished, with the Cubans closing in on him from both directions it was the only thing left to do.

Wiping the sweat from his eyes, he climbed the railings and stepped on to the nearest of the girders. With his arms outstretched like a tightrope walker, he began to make his way slowly and carefully towards the platform.

Thinking it was part of the entertainment offered by Seaquarium, the crowd began to applaud.

The applause swelled, for now Morales had pulled himself up on to the other girder and had begun to follow Fitzpatrick across.

Although he guessed what had happened, Fitzpatrick did not allow himself to look back. Instead, he continued to walk steadily forward along the narrow beam – right foot in front of the left, left foot in front of the right, heel to toe, arms outstretched and his eyes fixed unwaveringly on the platform ahead.

Four more of the same slow, deliberate steps and he had arrived. Seizing hold of the handrail, he vaulted over on to the platform.

Morales turned his head to yell something at Sanchez. It was only a small movement, but it was enough to make him lose his balance. He fell slowly, cartwheeled once and belly-flopped, drenching a group of spectators hanging over the railings on the island side of the moat.

With Morales in the water, Fitzpatrick now felt confident to tackle Sanchez. But where was he? When he had last seen him, Sanchez had been retracing his steps to intercept him as he came off the gantry.

Using his Dunhill lighter and three coins as an improvised knuckle-duster, Fitzpatrick set out to find him.

Morales, in the meantime, had surfaced. He flicked his long black hair out of his eyes, and, in an attempt to cover his embarrassment, began waving cheerfully to the crowd.

Although they knew what he didn't know – that he had fallen into the Man-eating Shark Channel – few showed any signs of alarm. Had he cried for help or showed even the slightest sign of distress, they would have reacted differently. As it was they did nothing, many having already watched divers hand-feeding manta rays, moray eels and giant sea bass with heads like bulldogs, as well as a man riding on the back of a killer whale.

Treading water, Morales turned and looked around him. It was not going to be easy to get out of the 25-foot-wide moat, he realized. There were no steps, and the sheer concrete on either side rose at least four feet above the surface of the water.

But then he noticed that below the bridge he had crossed there was a pipe linking the island with the mainland. This, he decided, was what he should head for. Once there, he'd be able to pull himself up on to the pipe, and from the pipe it would be easy enough to swing up on to the bridge.

As Morales struck out for the bridge, a small boy in the crowd began tugging his father's jacket. 'Hey, Pop, why's the man in the water?'

Knowing he would get no peace until he offered something in the way of an explanation, his father replied with the first

126

thing that came into his head: 'Guess he's goin' to demonstrate how shark-repellent works . . .'

The word spread quickly. Mothers began picking up the children for a better view, and everyone with a camera got ready to record what promised to be the highlight of their visit.

The first of the sharks to react to Morales was a 14-foot-long Tiger cruising on the opposite side of the moat. It turned lazily, its broad, dark back marbled with reflections of the sunlight sparkling on the surface of the blue water. With its great sickle-shaped tail moving almost imperceptibly, it began to home in on the source of the vibrations it could feel through the clusters of sensory cells running down either side of its body.

An excited murmur rose from the crowd as it swung into view, its dark dorsal fin cutting the water with barely a ripple.

Morales turned to see what the crowd was looking at and almost fainted.

Treading water, he watched horrified as the great dark shadow glided past him less than three feet to his right, made a tight turn and passed him again on the other side.

During his fall, he had grazed his ankle on the steel girder. It was the smallest of abrasions, and what little blood had oozed from under the broken skin had diffused instantly in the water.

Although Morales was unaware of his injury, the Tiger was not. Like all sharks, it was able to detect blood even when diluted to a concentration of one part to $1\frac{1}{2}$ million parts of water.

The creature swung around and made another pass, this time so close that it set Morales bobbing. A great 'Ole!' rose from the delighted crowd.

An elderly woman in Bermuda shorts turned to the man leaning over the railings next to her. 'Gee, I sure hope he's all right,' she said. 'You don't think maybe someone should call an attendant?'

The man took a bite of his ice-cream cone. 'Relax, lady,' he replied in a thick Texas drawl. 'If there'd bin a problem, someone would've called one by now.'

The Texan's wife leaned over the railings to smile reassuringly at the old lady. 'We saw a guy wrastle an alligator at

Tropical Paradise yesterday,' she said. 'I guess if you can get away with that, you can get away with anything!'

The Tiger brushed past Morales, bloodying the palm of his right hand with its sandpaper-rough skin, and turned again. This time, however, its dorsal fin sank below the surface, and, leaving a trail of turbulent water in its wake, it launched itself at his dangling legs. White protective membranes slid up over its eyes as its enormous jaws yawned open, then snapped like a steel trap over Morales's left hip.

As the Tiger dragged him screaming into the middle of the moat, other sharks began to appear from both directions.

Stunned with shock, it was only now that the crowd started to react. While some tried to shield their children's eyes, others began pelting the creatures with anything to hand – life-belts, Coca-Cola cans, even cameras and shoes.

It was all to no avail. Within seconds the water had been churned to a bloody froth as the frenzied sharks fought for what remained of Morales's body.

20

'Today, another folder bearing a red fatality tag was added to the International Shark Attack File at the Mote Marine Laboratory, Florida,' said the television newsreader, after finishing a report about an outbreak of gang warfare in Chicago. 'The victim's name: Angel Morales. Location: the Man-eating Shark Channel of the Miami Seaquarium!'

Lippencott waited a moment to make sure that the report which followed was the one they had seen on the 6 o'clock news, then reached across and switched off the set.

'Okay,' he said, turning to Fitzpatrick. 'So what happened when you realized you'd lost Sanchez?'

'Not a lot. I was on my way back to grab Morales as he came out of the water when I heard what had happened.' He shrugged. 'I guess I should've gone to the cops there and then. Except I figured I'd do better following it through myself rather than sitting around in some station house for half the night being asked questions I couldn't answer . . .'

Lippencott's girlfriend stubbed out her cigarette and got up. A psychiatric nurse at Jackson Memorial Hospital, Linda Hewatt was slim and small-boned, with an attractive, boyish face, freckles and short red hair. 'I'm going to change and do something about making up a bed for Mike,' she announced, smoothing down the skirt of her white uniform. 'Then I'll start fixing dinner. Is that okay with you guys?'

Fitzpatrick began apologizing for the trouble he was putting them to, but they would have none of it.

'Listen, with Sanchez still on the loose,' said Lippencott, 'you're going to be a helluva lot safer here than in a hotel.'

Linda agreed. 'I'm just sorry the place is in such a mess,' she said, looking around the room as if seeing it for the first time. Apart from the television set, a settee and a pair of easy chairs, the only things there were a couple of model ships in glass cases, a brass bridge telegraph, and a great many still unhung nautical prints. 'But as I guess Ed's told you, we haven't been in the house long, and with both of us working it's kinda hard to get things together as quickly as we'd have liked.'

There was a ring on the doorbell. 'That'll be Dick Buchanan,' said Lippencott.

Linda set out to answer it, but he stopped her. 'Better let me, honey,' he said, getting up and drawing a Smith and Wesson Centennial Airweight from a holster hanging over the back of the settee. 'Just in case . . .'

Lippencott returned a moment later with his second-in-command, a plump, genial man who, although it had only been an hour since they'd last met, insisted on giving Fitzpatrick another of his bone-crushing handshakes.

'Your luggage is in the hall,' he told him. 'There were a couple of messages from your office asking you to call, also one from Pierce timed at 2.30.

'Oh, and another thing,' he added, digging down into the breast pocket of his plaid jacket for a Western Union cablegram. 'This arrived for you while I was there . . .'

Lippencott broke open a six-pack of Schlitz and tossed a can to Buchanan. 'Mike, what about you?'

He looked up. 'Sorry?'

'Another beer?'

'No, thanks all the same,' he replied, turning back to the cablegram. 'I'll be *damned*!'

'Trouble?' Buchanan asked.

'Listen to this – it's from my office: "CANST UPCHASE SEA-QUARIUM SHARK ATTACK STORY FOR FIRST EDITION TODAY STOP HAVE PIX STOP"!'

Lippencott began to laugh. 'What're you going to do about it?'

Fitzpatrick crumpled the cablegram into a ball and tossed it into a wastepaper basket. 'I was out when it arrived, wasn't I? Anyway, if the agencies have wired them photographs, they'll already have a story . . .'

'Then why ask you to write another?'

'I suppose they think there's always a chance their own man'll come up with something the other papers haven't got . . . Christ, if they only *knew*!'

'You sure you don't want to call them?' asked Lippencott,

nodding at a telephone that was standing on top of a pile of directories in a corner of the room.

Fitzpatrick shook his head. 'Until I know how I'm going to play this thing, it's just too damned complicated.'

'Okay,' said Lippencott, 'then why don't we take our drinks outside and try to decide just what the hell we *are* going to do?'

He crossed the room, opened one of the glass sliding doors and led them out on to a redwood deck. Grouped beneath the kumquat tree that was growing up through a hole in the planking were several pieces of patio furniture still cocooned in their original plastic wrapping. The house overlooked Biscayne Bay, and beyond an expanse of newly laid turf bordered by shore juniper was a wooden jetty. Berthed alongside the jetty was what Linda had earlier described (somewhat huffily, Fitzpatrick had thought) as the apple of Lippencott's eye – an ocean-going cabin cruiser. Named after Raymond Chandler's private-eye hero, the *Marlowe* was long and sleek and white, with an uncluttered foredeck surrounded by high guardrails, a raked wheelhouse with panoramic vision, and a sundeck aft.

Buchanan opened his can of beer and took a long pull. 'So, have they picked up Sanchez yet?' he asked, as soon as they'd sat down.

'Nope!' Lippencott replied, making a grab at a mosquito that had begun to buzz him.

Buchanan loosened his tie. 'And what about Mike? How hard are they looking for Mike?'

'They're looking. But from what I could find out downtown, the description they're working with would fit ten thousand other guys.'

'I had a word with the desk clerk, not that it was of much help,' Buchanan explained. 'He *thinks* somebody asked for Mike earlier today, but he swears he can't remember telling them where he was going.'

'He's lying,' said Lippencott indignantly. 'If he didn't tell 'em, who did?'

'I suppose it's *just* possible that they were in the lobby when I was asking the way to Seaquarium,' Fitzpatrick suggested.

Lippencott didn't think it likely. 'If they were, how come it took them so long to find you?'

'All right, but if neither Morales nor Sanchez *were* in the lobby, how did they know what I looked like?'

'Umm . . .' Lippencott began stroking his beard thoughtfully. 'Mike, apart from us, who else knows where you were staying in Miami?'

'Half-a-dozen people at my office, my parents, Reggie Atwell – that's about it . . .'

'And presumably you've no reason to think that any of them, or us, would have hired a couple of Cuban heavies to pick you up?'

Fitzpatrick managed a smile. 'Hardly . . .'

Lippencott took out a panatella and began removing the cellophane wrapper. 'I think what happened was this,' he continued. 'Pierce gets the message that you've called, and calls Morales. He and Sanchez arrive at your hotel shortly after you'd left and ask for you. The desk clerk tells them you're out and where you've gone. Maybe they slipped him a couple of bucks or maybe they didn't; either way it's not significant.

'But what *is* significant—' he dropped the cellophane wrapper into an empty plant pot and reached across for his lighter '—what is significant is that – as you suggest – they don't need to have you paged at Seaquarium in order to find you. They're able to walk straight up to you.

'Which means they *must* have been carrying your photograph. And who would've given it to them? It can only be Pierce!'

He paused to light his panatella. 'But the *really* interesting question is this: where does Pierce get the photograph?'

Fitzpatrick was the first to offer a suggestion. 'From Clair?'

Lippencott nodded grimly. 'Of course!' He turned to Buchanan. 'Dick, you've got a buddy in the Medical Examiner's Office, haven't you?'

'A guy called Zuckerman. Jesse Zuckerman . . .'

'Do you think Zuckerman would tell you whether or not they've found any photographs among Morales's effects?'

'Morales's *effects*?' Buchanan looked dumbfounded. 'What effects? The guy was eaten by sharks, for chrissake!'

'I know he was,' said Lippencott, a trace of impatience in his voice. 'But you don't think they're going to leave them in Sea-quarium to quietly digest the poor bastard, do you?'

'I guess not.' Buchanan began to get up. 'You want me to call him?'

'Hold it a minute. If there is a photograph and it was Morales and not *Sanchez* who was carrying it, what are the chances of them letting you take a peek?'

Buchanan shrugged. 'I don't see why they shouldn't . . .'

'They won't ask too many questions?'

'Nothing I can't handle.'

Lippencott turned back to Fitzpatrick. 'If you're agreeable, what I think we do is this,' he said. 'If we find Morales *was* carrying a photograph of you, we go to the police, okay. If he wasn't – well then I don't know what to do . . . Try and get to see Pierce tomorrow, I guess . . .'

When Buchanan returned to the deck five minutes later he was rubbing his hands gleefully. 'Listen you guys, I think we struck oil! Morales *was* carrying photographs, and from Jesse's description they sound as if they might be of Mike. There's a girl in one of them, and in the other the guy's holding a dog.'

'Do you have a dog?' asked Lippencott.

Fitzpatrick nodded. 'I used to. Was it an Alsatian?'

'He just said it was a dog,' replied Buchanan with a shrug. 'A big dog . . .'

'Well, what are you waiting for?' asked Lippencott. 'Get your ass over there and see what gives!'

After promising each other that they would meet for lunch soon, Zuckerman led Buchanan through a maze of passageways to a room at the back of the Dade County Medical Examiner's Office.

'By the way,' said Zuckerman, before opening the door. 'The name of the guy performing the autopsy is Mitchell. Ross Mitchell.' He nodded approvingly. 'He's okay . . .'

The brilliantly lit room contained an X-ray machine, several glass-fronted instrument cases, wash-basins, and three huge enamelled examination tables, each overhung by a weighing

133

machine, a microphone, a shower fitment and a suction appliance. Grouped around the table nearest the door were half-a-dozen men wearing green scrub suits, rubber aprons and boots.

The eldest of the men looked over the top of a pair of glasses taped to the bridge of his nose by a Band-Aid. 'Hi there, guys!' he called. 'C'mon in.'

Zuckerman introduced everyone, and then with a cheerful 'Have fun!' to Buchanan, left for the night.

Trying not to breathe too deeply, Buchanan moved further into the room.

'Nasty business this,' said Mitchell, wrinkling his nose at what was on the table. 'Jesse tells me you'd been investigating the guy . . .'

As Buchanan opened his mouth to reply, one of the other men turned to put something on the weighing machine, suddenly exposing him to a sight of the dead Cuban. 'Christ *Almighty*!' he exclaimed.

Morales was in at least eight pieces, each piece placed more or less in its correct position relative to the others. Attached to each of the pieces was a buff-coloured label bearing what Buchanan assumed to be the Latin name of the shark from whose stomach it had been taken.

At the far end of the table was Morales's severed head; one of his eyes was missing and most of the flesh had been torn from the left-hand side of his face, revealing a gleaming gold eyetooth. Below lay his shattered thorax, his arms, part of a hand, several fingers and a thumb. The right leg was still attached to his empty pelvis, and, apart from a semi-circle of deep triangular punctures in the upper thigh, it was unmarked. However, most of the flesh had been stripped from his detached left leg, and it was without a foot.

'Well, I reckon there's something like thirty pounds of our friend still unaccounted for,' the man announced, as he lifted a bag full of remnants off the weighing machine and plopped it back on to the table.

Mitchell shrugged. 'So we tell the coroner we think he's been on a diet,' he said, winking at Buchanan. 'Now, Jesse tells me you want to take a look over the deceased's effects, right?'

'If that's okay with you . . .'

'Be my guest!'

Buchanan was taken across to a stainless-steel instrument table on which lay a Browning P-35 automatic and the tattered remains of its holster, a heavy gold cigarette case bent almost in two, a bunch of keys on a *Playboy* key ring, a Rolex Oyster wristwatch that he noticed was still working, and a black crocodile-skin billfold beside which were a number of credit cards, a driving licence, about $200 in assorted bills, and two curled-up Polaroid prints.

Buchanan uncurled the first photograph. It was of Morales and a tall, dark-haired young man wearing a flower-patterned shirt and sunglasses – a man who might well have been Fitzpatrick. But was it? Buchanan couldn't be sure.

The second photograph was a close-up of the same man, standing alongside a girl holding a spaniel. This time, however, the man had removed his sunglasses to reveal a pair of small, closely set eyes similar to those of Morales.

Buchanan was no longer in any doubt; the man was quite definitely not Michael Fitzpatrick.

21

Martha Pierce lived in one of the older apartment blocks on the west side of Collins Avenue, and, after an armed security guard had telephoned to announce their arrival, Lippencott and Fitzpatrick took the elevator to the penthouse floor.

By the time they arrived, she was at the door of her apartment, looking cool and composed in a white, raw-silk trouser suit and tortoise-shell sunglasses.

'Mr Lippencott I already know,' she said, offering him one of her well manicured hands. 'This, then, must be Mr Fitzpatrick.'

Leaving a trail of Guerlain's *Chant d'Aromes* in her wake, she led them into an enormous drawing-room decorated in a style that was eclectic to the point of eccentricity and overwhelmingly grandiose. There were Louis XV-style sofas and chairs, a grand piano decorated with gilt *appliqués*, and a Regency centre table with a top supported by three intertwined gold dragons. The walls were crowded with eighteenth-century flower paintings in gilt rococo frames, and hanging from the high coffered ceiling were a pair of enormous crystal chandeliers.

Suddenly Fitzpatrick understood why Lippencott was wearing a suit and tie.

From the drawing-room, they were led on to a tiled terrace filled with tubs of flowering shrubs and orange trees heavy with golden fruit. In one corner, a white cockatoo sat preening itself on a stand.

'Please,' she said, indicating that they were to sit at an ornate wicker table that had been set for tea.

As if on cue, a uniformed coloured maid appeared with a heavily laden silver tray.

'Tell me, Mr Fitzpatrick,' said Pierce, busying herself with the bone-china tea things, 'is there any news of your young friend yet?'

'I'm afraid not,' he replied, feeling very ill at ease. Although Lippencott had described Pierce and her apartment accurately enough, he had not prepared him for someone quite so regal. Suddenly the idea that she could possibly have had anything to do with Clair's disappearance, much less what had happened at Seaquarium, seemed ludicrous.

Pierce shook her head sadly, and after passing out cups of Lapsang Souchong, began telling Fitzpatrick the same story she had told Lippencott on the previous Wednesday.

As soon as she had finished, he said: 'Since Mr Lippencott called on you, I've been back to see the gentleman who led us to you in the first place.

'I'm sorry to have to tell you this, but he insists that it was Clair – Miss Tennant, that is – who he saw getting into your car . . .'

Pierce's hand went to her throat. 'Oh *dear*!' she said, seemingly very perplexed. 'How dreadful!'

'Can I just say this,' Fitzpatrick continued, choosing his words carefully. 'I'm not asking you to break any promise you might have made to Miss Tennant. If she's asked you not to tell me where she is, clearly you're in – well, you're in a very difficult position—'

Pierce stopped him with a touch of her hand on his sleeve. 'Forgive me, Mr Fitzpatrick, but I think I understand what it is you're trying to say.

'Believe me, if I *did* know where Miss Tennant was I'd at least endeavour to set your mind at rest. But as Mr Lippencott will already have explained, I'm afraid I've never met the young lady.

'I only wish I had,' she added wistfully. 'She sounds quite charming.'

Lippencott cleared his throat. 'Do you know a man called Angel Morales, ma'am?'

'Angel Morales?' Pierce considered the question for a moment. 'I'm sure I don't, yet the name does *seem* to ring a bell . . .' She paused to take a sip of tea. 'Wait a minute!' A disturbing thought seemed to have surfaced in her mind. 'Wasn't Morales the man who was killed at Seaquarium a few days ago?'

Lippencott nodded.

'But according to the newspapers, he was a convicted

criminal!' she said, as if affronted by the suggestion that she might have known such a person. She began fingering one of her gold ear-rings unhappily. 'Oh dear, this is getting to be rather embarrassing . . . I take it you think that he, too, might have been involved in Miss Tennant's disappearance?'

'It's possible, ma'am,' replied Lippencott gravely. 'Very possible.'

'I see . . .' After staring down into her teacup for a while, she suddenly stood up. 'Would you gentlemen excuse me for a moment?'

Such was the effect she created, that even Lippencott – who rarely went in for displays of old-world courtliness – half rose from his chair as she left the table.

When she returned she was carrying a copy of the *Washington Post*. 'Please don't get up,' she said, handing Lippencott the paper. She pointed to an item she had marked with a purple cross. 'Perhaps I could ask you to read that . . .'

The story was about how more and more business corporations – in an attempt to reduce white collar crime – were using lie-detectors when screening job applicants.

'Oh, come now, ma'am,' he said, passing the paper to Fitzpatrick. 'There's no question of us asking you to take a lie-detector test, if that's what you're thinking!'

'But if I don't take such a test, how can you possibly know whether I'm telling the truth or not?'

'By asking your friends in London – the people you had dinner with the night Miss Tennant disappeared – to corroborate your story . . .'

Pierce began fingering her ear-ring again. 'That's precisely what I was hoping to avoid,' she said, pleasantly enough. 'Although I'm sure you'd handle it with the utmost tact, I'd still rather my friends didn't know I was being – well, that I was being *investigated*.'

Lippencott nodded understandingly. 'Well, it doesn't necessarily have to be me who talks to them,' he pointed out. 'Mr Fitzpatrick could perfectly well do that when he gets back next week.'

Pierce smiled disarmingly at Fitzpatrick. 'If you'll forgive me for saying so, having a member of the press ask them such questions isn't really much better.

'No, I'm sure the best idea is the Poly—' She hesitated, apparently unable to remember the word.

Lippencott came to her rescue. 'Poly*graph*.'

'Polygraph!' She smiled her thanks, and as Lippencott and Fitzpatrick exchanged puzzled glances, went on to say brightly: 'Just let me tell my story to the Polygraph and we'll clear up the whole matter in next to no time and without having to bother anyone else!

'Now,' she added, apparently unaware of the effect she had created, 'who would like some more tea?'

22

'Hi there, fella!' cried Russell Yuncker, striding across the thickly carpeted reception area to pump Lippencott's hand. 'Long time no see!'

Yuncker was a vice-president of the management-recruitment agency where Pierce was to take her lie-detector test in fifteen minutes' time. He was tall and slim, with a pale, foxy face and red hair that had begun to thin at the crown. A gold watchchain with a Phi Beta Kappa key hung from the waistcoat pockets of an impeccably cut, grey herring-bone suit, and he had on a pair of highly polished brown brogues.

After he had been introduced to Fitzpatrick, he led them into a room which, after the bustling reception area, seemed quiet and remote as a sensory-deprivation chamber. Clad with acoustic tiles, the room was windowless and contained only a mirror, a few chairs and a table on which was mounted the Polygraph – a large, matt-grey metal box with dials and a roll of graph paper on which rested three pens.

They sat down, and, after Yuncker and Lippencott had spent several minutes catching up on what each had been doing since they had last met, Lippencott said: 'Okay, so is there anything else you need to know about this case?'

Clasping his big, bony hands behind his head, Yuncker pondered the question for a moment. 'I don't think so. Either Pierce is lying or she isn't. If she is, she's telling a whopper, in which case—' he nodded at the apparatus in front of him '—there's no way she's going to be able to hide it from this baby. No way.'

'I'm not at all sure she *is* lying,' said Lippencott unhappily. 'I've got a nasty feeling the whole thing's going to turn out to be a waste of time and money. Have *you* ever heard of anyone asking to take a lie-detector test in a situation where they knew they were going to have to lie?'

Yuncker shook his head. 'If it comes to that, I've never heard of anyone asking to take a lie-detector test to prove that she's not covering for a chick who's walked out on her boyfriend. Hell, it's not exactly a federal offence . . .'

A light had begun flashing on his intercom, and he leaned forward and pressed down a switch. 'Yeah?'

'Mrs Martha Pierce is here for her two-thirty appointment.'

'Tell her I'll be right out,' Yuncker replied. 'Oh, and honey, no more calls for the next hour, huh?'

Yuncker released the switch and sprang to his feet.

'You want us to move next door?' asked Lippencott.

'If you don't mind,' replied Yuncker, crossing to take down a white coat that was hanging behind the door. 'But don't worry,' he told Fitzpatrick, 'we're wired for sound in here, and that—' he nodded at the mirror '—that's one-way glass, so you won't miss any of the action.'

Pierce arrived in the room Lippencott and Fitzpatrick had just left, dressed as for the paddock at Longchamp. Through the one-way glass they watched as she took off her picture hat and long white gloves and sat down in a chair next to the Polygraph. Then, after Yuncker had explained what would be happening and had got her to sign a form stating that she would hold no claim against either him or his company whatever the outcome of the test, he opened a notebook and asked her to tell him in as much detail as possible where she had been and what she had done on the night Clair disappeared.

The story she told was identical in every respect to the one she had told previously.

'Fine,' said Yuncker, coming around from behind the table. 'Now let's get you hooked up to the machine.'

'What do these do?' she asked, as he placed two black, corrugated rubber tubes across her chest, one above her breasts and the other below.

'Measure changes in your breathing rhythm,' he replied, attaching the tubes to fixtures on the side of the chair. 'And this—' he began attaching another instrument to the palm of her right hand '—this measures any variations in the output of perspiration.'

He turned and picked up a blood-pressure cuff. 'You'll have

come across one of these before,' he said, wrapping it tightly around her left forearm. 'However, we'll be using it to measure any *changes* which occur to your pulse rate and blood pressure.'

He inflated the cuff and straightened up. 'How does that feel? Comfortable?'

'It feels fine.'

'Good. Now try to relax, look straight ahead at the wall, and answer all of my questions with either a yes or a no. Is that quite clear? Either a yes or a no.' Yuncker moved out of her line of vision, sat down and switched on the machine, setting the roll of graph paper slowly turning.

After he had asked a number of test questions and made some adjustments to the controls, he picked up his pen and said: 'Very well, Mrs Pierce, I think we're ready to begin . . .'

Speaking slowly and in a voice devoid of emotion, Yuncker asked one question after another, Pierce replying with either a yes or a no. Throughout, he kept his eyes fixed on the pattern of wavy red lines being drawn by the three pens on the slowly turning roll of graph paper, making a note each time he asked a question.

Finally he asked: 'Have you answered all of my questions truthfully?'

'Yes,' Pierce replied without hesitation.

Yuncker switched off the machine, and after spending several minutes silently working his way back along the great loops of graph paper, said: 'If you don't mind, there are a couple of questions I'd like to ask again. Then we really *are* through. Are you still comfortable?'

Pierce assured him that she was.

'Good.' He switched on the machine again and cleared his throat. 'Have you ever engaged the services of Angel Morales?'

'No,' Pierce replied firmly.

Yuncker made a note on the graph paper.

'Have you ever engaged the services of Pedro Sanchez?'

'No.'

'Has anyone ever engaged the services of either man on your behalf?'

'No.'

'Have you at any time met either Morales or Sanchez?'

'No.'

'Thank you,' he said, non-committally. 'Now a couple of questions about the evening of August 12.

'Was Clair Tennant one of the friends with whom you had dinner on the evening of August 12 last?'

'How could it have been?' Pierce protested. 'I told you, I've never—'

'Just answer either yes or no,' Yuncker said impassively. 'I'll ask the question again: was Clair Tennant one of the friends with whom you had dinner on the evening of August 12?'

'*No!*'

'Did you and your friends have grouse for dinner?'

'Yes.'

'Did you pay for the dinner?'

'Yes.'

'After dinner, did you and your friends visit Clair Tennant?'

'No.'

'Did you visit Clair Tennant alone?'

'No.'

'Have you answered all of my questions truthfully?'

'Yes.'

Yuncker switched off the machine and stood up. 'Thank you, Mrs Pierce, you've been most patient and co-operative.'

For a moment she didn't react.

'Mrs Pierce? We're through . . .'

She looked surprised. 'Are we really?'

'We are,' said Yuncker, bending down to deflate the blood-pressure cuff. 'Thank you for giving us so much of your time.'

'Well, how did I do?'

'I'll need a little time to check through the results,' he explained, removing the attachment from her hand. 'But I'm sure Mr Lippencott will be able to let you know something within the next day or so.'

After Yuncker had removed the pneumatic tubes from around her chest, she got up, crossed to the mirror through which the others were watching, and began putting on her hat.

'Now, can I get you a drink of some sort?' he asked.

Smiling sweetly, she turned and picked up her gloves and her handbag. 'That's most kind of you, but if you don't mind I think perhaps I'd better be on my way.'

When Yuncker entered the adjoining room after seeing her to the elevator, he was carrying three paper cups full of machine coffee. He handed one to Lippencott and another to Fitzpatrick, then flopped down into a chair and began unbuttoning his waistcoat.

'Well?' asked Lippencott.

Yuncker cracked his knuckles. 'I guess I'd better take another look through it,' he replied, nodding wearily at the great heap of unwound graph paper they could see through the one-way glass, 'but it looks very much as if she's been telling the truth, the whole truth and nothing but the truth from start to finish!'

23

When Fitzpatrick got back from interviewing Mancini on Hippocrates Cay, he found Lippencott on board the *Marlowe*, putting a new spool of chart paper into the echo-sounder.

'Since tomorrow's your last day, I thought we might take a run down to the Keys.' Lippencott turned and smiled. 'How does that sound to you?'

'Sounds great!' Fitzpatrick took off his blazer and threw it on to the wheelhouse bench.

'So, how did it go today?'

'Fine . . .'

'You don't sound too certain.'

'It was fine,' Fitzpatrick assured him. 'No problems.'

Lippencott crossed to the chart table and opened a drawer. 'What was the name of that island again?' he asked, beginning to thumb through a pile of charts.

'Hippocrates Cay.'

'That's what I thought you said. And it's off the eastern coast of Abaco?'

'Right. Near Treasure Cay.'

Lippencott pushed the drawer shut with his hips. 'I'm damned if I could find anything marked Hippocrates Cay,' he grumbled, spreading one of the charts on the table.

Fitzpatrick crossed to look with him. 'That's it,' he said pointing to one of the tiny islands enclosed within a purple box. 'Snaith renamed it, and I guess they haven't got around to doing an update yet.'

'How did you get there? By seaplane?'

'Helicopter from Watson Park.'

Lippencott put away the chart and hoisted himself up on to the chart table. 'And how did you make out with Mancini?'

'He was good value. *Very* good value. I might even try to get across to New York and do a follow-up piece after he's had his transplant.'

'And what about Snaith? Did you get to meet him?'

'Very briefly. He looked in for a drink just before lunch.'

Lippencott raised his eyebrows expectantly. 'And?'

'I don't know . . .' Perplexed, Fitzpatrick reached across for his blazer and took out a pack of Camels and a lighter. 'Snaith's one of those guys who never quite looks you straight in the eye. In fact, I thought he was a bit spooky . . .' He paused to light his cigarette. 'If it comes to that, there was something a bit spooky about the whole place. It sounds crazy, but all the time I had the feeling I was being watched . . .'

Lippencott shrugged. 'It's not so crazy. You probably *were* being watched. Don't forget, the clinic's unique selling proposition – as they say on Madison Avenue – is its security.'

'Could be . . . As a matter of fact, I noticed that some of the plants growing near the foreshore had electrodes stuck to their leaves. I think they're probably being used as – and don't laugh – stress alarm indicators.'

Lippencott laughed. 'What the hell's a stress alarm indicator?'

'Well . . .' Fitzpatrick paused to collect his thoughts. 'Okay, does the name *Backster* mean anything to you? Cleve Backster?'

'Not a thing.'

'Well, Backster – who used to be with the CIA before starting a school to train police officers in the use of lie-detectors – one day decided to hook up the office rubber plant with a Polygraph to see if he could time how long it took water to rise from the root to the leaf.'

'I have days like that, too,' said Lippencott, bending to tighten the laces on one of his deck shoes.

'Don't we all! Anyway,' Fitzpatrick continued, 'when he found he wasn't getting anywhere, he began wondering what would happen if he were to *burn* one of the leaves. Straight away, the Polygraph went berserk. It was as if the plant had somehow managed to read his mind . . .'

'Ah!' Lippencott nodded. 'Now I know who you're talking about. This was – what? – back in the late '60s.'

'Right. Backster's first paper – called something like "Primary Perception in Plant Life" – was published in 1968. Since then, a lot of work has been done on the interaction between people and plants. For instance, at the Institute of Psycholo-

146

gical Sciences in Moscow they claim to have produced scientifically verifiable evidence that plants *do* respond to a wide range of human emotions. Also, there have been stories about the US Army experimenting with plants as stress alarm indicators.'

Lippencott looked amused. 'And you think Snaith's got all the plants on Hippocrates Cay wired into Polygraphs?'

'I can't think of another reason for attaching *electrodes* to their leaves . . .'

'Didn't you ask him?'

'I didn't notice the damn things until I was on my way back to the chopper.' As the wash from a passing sport fisherman with a flying bridge and a fighting chair set the *Marlowe* bobbing gently at her moorings, Fitzpatrick crossed to the wheelhouse door and flipped his cigarette into the water. 'There's another reason why I think they're probably being used as stress alarm indicators,' he said, returning to his seat. 'At fifty-yard intervals along the entire shoreline, there're what look like lamp standards carrying TV cameras and what I'm pretty sure are infra-red floodlights.'

'Again, I'm not surprised,' said Lippencott. 'If anyone was going to hit the island, they'd almost certainly come in by boat.'

'Ah, but wait a minute; there must be at least a hundred of these posts. That means a hundred monitors, and – what? – men watching sets of four monitors each. That's a twenty-five-man team on duty twenty-four hours a day, which means – assuming each team works an eight-hour day – *seventy-five men*!' Fitzpatrick shook his head. 'It just doesn't make sense!

'However,' he continued, 'if there was a way of detecting anyone coming ashore *intent* on doing a mischief, you could get away with, say, eight monitors and six men . . .'

'I see what you mean,' said Lippencott. 'The plants in the sector where the landing was taking place would react; their reaction would be recorded on the Polygraph . . .'

Fitzpatrick nodded encouragingly. 'And the Polygraph would activate the TV cameras and infra-red floodlights in the appropriate sector. Infra-red light is invisible to the human eye, so the kidnappers wouldn't know they'd been spotted until the security guards moved in on them . . .'

'You know what I think?' said Lippencott. 'I think it's bull-shit! Sure, it's unlikely that Snaith's employing seventy-five guys just to sit around on their butts watching TV monitors. However, I think the cameras and the lights and the electrodes – I think they're nothing more than a fancy version of the phoney burglar alarms some guys put outside their houses.'

'Maybe. But if I'm right – and I must say, Snaith didn't strike me as the sort of guy who'd do anything that wasn't for real – he knows a hell of a lot about Polygraphs.'

'Now, Pierce works for Snaith, and she asked – *asked*, remember – to take a lie-detector test which "proved" she had nothing to do with Clair's disappearance. Except deep down, neither of us really believes her.'

Lippencott drew in his breath sharply. 'I'm not sure I'd—'

'Hold it a *minute*, Ed!' said Fitzpatrick, suddenly making a grab for his blazer. 'Jesus, something else has just occurred to me!' He took out his diary and began leafing frantically through the pages. 'Trying to think of something to say to Snaith – and believe me, talking to him was like trying to hold a conversation with an I Speak Your Weight machine – I asked what it was he missed most about England. He said something about – I don't know – some nonsense about ripe Stilton steeped in port and well-hung grouse. He *definitely* mentioned well-hung grouse . . .'

'What the hell's well-hung grouse got to do with telepathic plants and Polygraphs?'

'Listen, Pierce said that on the night Clair disappeared – the night of August the 12th – she was having dinner with friends. She was able to remember everything about that evening, including the fact that she'd had *grouse*.' He handed the diary to Lippencott. 'But just take a look at what it says in the August 12th panel!'

Lippencott began reading aloud. ' "Lunch NPL 1.30—" '

'No, no, no! Look at what's printed alongside the date . . .'

' "Grouse shooting begins".' He tried again, shifting the emphasis as though that would, in some mysterious way, solve the riddle. 'I still don't get it . . .'

'You don't?' said Fitzpatrick, as if it were glaringly obvious.

148

'Look, Pierce said she had grouse on the 12th, right? But if the season didn't *start* until the 12th, how the hell could she?'

'Maybe it was shot on the morning of the 12th,' replied Lippencott, stifling a yawn.

'Ah, but that's just it: in Britain, grouse is never eaten until it's been left to hang at least a week! That's what Snaith meant when he talked about "well-hung grouse"!'

'Jesus!' Lippencott began to look interested. 'That was one of the questions Yuncker asked Pierce while she was hooked up to the Polygraph!'

'Are you sure?'

'Positive. But are you sure about this grouse thing?'

'I'm pretty sure . . .'

Lippencott thought for a moment. 'You know, Yuncker fancies himself as something of a gourmet . . . Why don't I give him a call,' he said, jumping off the chart table to disappear out through the wheelhouse door.

Fitzpatrick began to pace up and down. If Pierce had lied about the grouse while she was being tested, why had it gone undetected?

And why had he been so unsettled to think that Snaith might be an expert on lie-detectors? He knew that it had something to do with the fact that the Institute of Psychological Sciences had used lie-detectors when testing the interaction between people and plants. But what?

Suddenly it came to him: in order to induce emotions on demand, the Russian experimenters had hypnotized their subjects.

Almost simultaneously, the first recollection triggered a second – something about secret agents and hypnosis . . . Something Dr Pohl had mentioned on the night he had tried to hypnotize de Souza.

Of course! Pohl had said that a cover story learned under hypnosis would be unshakeable, because, as far as the agent was concerned, *the cover story would be the true story*.

Finally, the jigsaw seemed to be coming together. Pierce had asked for a lie-detector test because she knew she could outwit it, which could only mean that she had played a significant part in Clair's deciding to leave. And if Pierce was capable of being hypnotized so effectively that she could outwit a lie-detector, why couldn't hypnosis have been used to induce Clair to leave?

A moment later Lippencott reappeared at the wheelhouse door, and, before he'd had a chance to speak, all of Fitzpatrick's newly evolved theories came tumbling out.

With growing unease, Lippencott waited for him to finish. 'It's very ingenious. But there's one thing wrong with it – grouse can either be eaten on the day it's shot, or after it's been left to hang for a week.

'So, there's absolutely no reason why Pierce shouldn't have had it – according to Yuncker, several London restaurants make a big thing of having grouse flown in from Scotland in time for dinner on the 12th!'

24

Yuncker took off his jacket, hung it carefully over the back of a chair in Lippencott's sitting-room and sat down. 'Okay,' he said, beginning to polish his sunglasses. 'Tell me what happened.'

'After Ed had rung you, I still felt uneasy,' Fitzpatrick explained. 'So I did what I should have done straight off – I called London and talked to the manager of the restaurant where Pierce had dinner.'

Yuncker nodded approvingly. 'Good thinking, fella,' he said, checking the lenses against the light. 'And he told you they never serve grouse?'

'They do – it's on the menu tonight. But it *wasn't* on the menu on the night of August 12th! He's absolutely definite about that. Hardly any London restaurants serve it on the 12th any more – air freighting it in from Scotland's got too damned expensive.'

Yuncker opened his briefcase and lifted out the roll of graph paper he had used while testing Pierce. 'I don't get it,' he said, unrolling the paper on the floor. 'I just do not get it. Because subjects more often than not screw up on the small details, I twice asked Pierce what it was she'd had for dinner. But look—' Now crouching down on his heels, he pointed first at a section of the trace in the middle of the roll, and another near the end. 'There's not a flicker! Not a goddamned flicker!

'Compare that with what happens when we know she's *not* telling the truth,' he continued, pointing at a section of the trace near the start of the roll, where, in order to establish parameters for the test, he had asked her to answer certain questions untruthfully. 'The pens are going every whichway!'

Linda, who, like Fitzpatrick and Lippencott, had got down on to the floor to look at the trace with Yuncker, crossed her legs under her and said: 'Maybe she's not actually *lying*, just not remembering correctly. I'm damned if I could remember what I'd had for dinner two weeks ago . . .'

Yuncker straightened up, stepped over the graph paper and

151

returned to his seat. 'That's only because nothing very exciting happened to you two weeks ago.'

'How did you know it didn't?' she asked, sounding slightly miffed.

'Well did it?'

She sighed. 'No, I guess not . . .'

'Tell me,' said Yuncker, 'what did you have the first time Ed took you out to dinner?'

'Hamburger!' she replied, feigning indignation. 'After we'd been to a drive-in movie, yet! I almost didn't go out with him again because of it!'

'Well there you go,' said Yuncker, satisfied that his point had been made.

Lippencott turned and winked at Fitzpatrick. 'I've always believed in beginning as I intend to go on,' he said, in an aside loud enough for Linda to hear.

Grinning, she leaned forward and tugged at his beard.

Lippencott scrambled to his feet and went to sit on the settee. 'Supposing Mike is right and Pierce was given her story under hypnosis,' he said to Yuncker. 'Would that have enabled her to beat the Polygraph?'

Yuncker cracked his knuckles. 'I suppose it's possible. Anything's *possible*. But we're back to the old question – why?'

Yuncker cracked his knuckles again, this time loudly enough to make Linda wince. 'Do you mind, fella, if I toss a couple of questions at you?' he asked Fitzpatrick.

'Go ahead.'

'Some of them are going to be pretty tough.'

Fitzpatrick sat down. 'Fire away . . .'

'Did Clair at any time work for a government department – the Ministry of Defence, for example?'

Fitzpatrick shook his head.

'Ever visited Russia, or any of the Eastern Bloc countries?'

'Never.'

'Was she into the drug scene in any way? Smoke grass, sniff coke – anything like that?'

'Not during the time I've known her . . .'

'Was she ever a hooker?'

'A *hooker*?' Fitzpatrick frowned. 'What the hell—' he began indignantly, but Lippencott stopped him.

'Hold your horses, Mike. These are all very relevant questions, and, frankly, they're ones I asked Reggie Atwell when he first called me.'

Having pacified Fitzpatrick, he turned back to Yuncker. 'Russ, this girl's so clean you could dress a wound with her.'

Yuncker looked as though he doubted whether anyone could be that unblemished. 'Atwell check her out at the Yard?'

With a guilty look at Fitzpatrick, Lippencott replied: 'He did . . .'

'Ummm.' Yuncker considered some other possibilities. 'Compulsory prostitution?' he sugggested, raising his eyebrows.

Lippencott shook his head. 'The wrong type, the wrong background, the wrong nationality.'

After several minutes during which no one spoke or moved, Yuncker suddenly got up. 'Mind if I make a call?'

Lippencott twisted around and pointed at the telephone, now standing on a table delivered the previous day. Seeing Yuncker hesitate, he said: 'Or there's one in the bedroom, if you'd rather . . .'

'Hold it!' cried Linda, scrambling to her feet. 'The room's in a mess!'

She rushed out, to return a couple of minutes later. 'Turn right at the top of the stairs,' she told Yuncker. 'It's the second door on your left.'

Shutting the door after him, she said to Lippencott: 'What was that all about?'

'Calling from another room?' He chuckled. 'Probably wants to talk to one of his CIA buddies . . .'

'CIA?' She frowned. 'What would he want to talk to the CIA about?'

'He used to work for them, honey. Probably still does, for all I know.'

'But you've always said he works for a management-recruitment agency . . .'

'He *does* work for a management-recruiting agency,' Lippencott replied, a trace of impatience in his voice. 'But that doesn't stop him from working for the CIA as well, and the CIA's funded more research into interrogation techniques than probably any other government agency. If they don't know how to handle a situation like this, no one does . . .'

With a shrug, Linda left the room again, this time announcing that she was going to make coffee.

When she returned five minutes later, Yuncker was still missing. She put down the tray, and, as she began pouring the steaming coffee, said to Lippencott: 'You know, I hate to say this about a buddy of yours, Ed, but I just can't get it up for that guy Yuncker. I mean, like he really gives me the heebie-jeebies!'

'That's only because you've discovered that he works for the CIA!'

'I've always felt that way about him.'

'You've *always* felt that way about him?' Lippencott began to protest that that wasn't true, but she stopped him with a nod in the direction of the door.

A moment later Yuncker re-entered the room, looking grim-faced and even paler than usual.

'Okay?' Lippencott asked.

'I guess so,' he said, taking a mug of coffee and returning to his seat. 'Well, it's certainly beginning to look as though Pierce might have been hypnotized, or that she hypnotized herself—'

'Hypnotized *herself*?' Lippencott looked at the others incredulously. 'How can anybody hypnotize themselves?'

Linda passed him a mug of coffee. 'That's not such a big deal,' she said, starting to roll a four-handed joint. 'Patients undergoing hypnotherapy are often taught autohypnosis as a means of alleviating symptoms of one sort or another.'

She paused to light the joint, took a deep pull and passed it to Lippencott. 'Also, it's increasingly being used in obstetrics to reduce both the duration and pain of labour.'

Yuncker nodded. 'And it's taught as part of US Air Force survival training programmes,' he added. 'So it can't be *all* that way out . . .'

'But if that's how Pierce managed to beat the Polygraph,' said Fitzpatrick, taking the joint from Lippencott, 'how the hell are we ever going to get the truth out of her?'

'Well?' Lippencott asked Yuncker.

He scratched the side of his face. 'There *is* a way . . .' he began, but seemed reluctant to continue.

Lippencott tried prompting him. 'Sodium pentothal?'

Yuncker shook his head. 'I suggested that, but by *itself* it's unlikely to do the trick,' he replied, waving away the offer of the joint.

'Well, what then?'

'ECT.'

'ECT?' Linda looked horrified. 'Electroconvulsive therapy? You'll never get her to agree to *that*!'

Yuncker laughed humourlessly. 'I know we won't get her to *agree* to it, honey . . .'

'For Christ's sake, Russ,' said Lippencott. 'This is worse than waiting for the other shoe to drop! What is it you have in mind?'

Yuncker got up, and with his hands in his pockets, ambled across to the window. With his back still to the room, he said: 'I'm just spitballing here, you understand, but supposing I could get hold of an ECT machine? Just *supposing* . . .'

Linda looked at Lippencott as if she expected him to order Yuncker from the house. When she saw that he intended to neither do nor say anything, she turned back to Yuncker, her thin face tightening menacingly. 'And then what?' she demanded.

'Give her a hundred volts through the frontal lobes,' Yuncker replied in a matter-of-fact tone. 'Then question her again.'

Linda exploded. 'You sonuvabitch!' she cried. 'How can you even *think* of doing anything so despicable?'

Snatching the joint from Lippencott, she scrambled to her feet, ran across the graph paper and out of the room, slamming the door behind her.

Yuncker spun round, his mouth gaping open. 'What did I say?' he asked, looking from one man to the other.

From upstairs came the sound of another door being slammed.

Wearily, Lippencott pulled himself up off the settee and started towards the door. 'I guess I'd better go talk to her,' he said. 'Oh, and Russ, when we get back, do me a favour – let's have no more talk about giving Pierce ECT, huh? I mean, man, it's not even like it's a *practical* proposition!'

'Not a practical proposition?' Yuncker looked affronted. 'What's *im*practicable about it? I can get hold of the hardware and the drugs, and Linda's a psychiatric nurse . . .'

'Now wait a minute!' said Fitzpatrick, alarmed at the turn the conversation had taken. 'Quite apart from any other considerations, how the hell were you proposing to get an ECT machine into Pierce's apartment?'

'Everything we'd need would go into a couple of small suitcases.'

Fitzpatrick tried again. 'Okay, but Pierce isn't going to lie back and think of England while you're putting the electrodes to her head!'

'So, we give her a shot of sodium pentothal first . . .'

Fitzpatrick looked despairingly at Lippencott.

'Giving her an injection wouldn't be too much of a hassle,' Lippencott admitted. 'As a matter of fact, when we had her under surveillance one of the things we discovered was that she has a nurse visit her every morning. According to the doorman – who got it from the maid – Pierce is in the middle of a cycle of injections. Hormones, or maybe it's vitamins. Anyway, shots of some sort.

'Oh, and incidentally,' he added, as he began moving around the room, switching on lights, 'the nurse arrives at seven-thirty – an hour before either the cleaning woman or the maid.'

Yuncker's watery eyes began to twinkle. 'I'm with you, fella,' he said. 'What you're thinking is that we could delay the regular nurse and have someone else go in instead. That someone tells Pierce the regular nurse is sick, and instead of giving her oestrogen or whatever the hell it is she's having, gives her a knock-out—'

'Hold it a minute!' said Lippencott firmly. He came back and sat down on the settee. 'Russ, I don't want to seem rude or ungrateful, but just let me ask you this: do you know what the fuck it is you're talking about? That's not intended to be a provocative question; I just don't *know* whether you do or not . . .'

'I'm not an *expert*, if that's what you mean . . .'

'But the guy you've just been talking to is?'

Yuncker nodded. 'We've been getting some of the best advice in the business . . .'

'I notice you keep using the word "we",' said Lippencott. 'Does this mean you intend to sit in on the gig?'

Yuncker shuffled uneasily. '*That* might be kinda difficult, fella—'

'All right, all right!' said Lippencott, in no mood for specious explanations. 'So, what're the risks?'

'To her or to you?'

'To her, of course! Jesus, I know what the risks are to *us*! You want me to list them for you?'

Yuncker held up his hand. 'Providing it's administered by someone who knows what they're doing – and that's where you'll need Linda – Pierce would be at less risk than when she's driving on a freeway. How old did you say she was?'

'Late forties.'

'Um . . .' Yuncker considered the implications. 'Well, if she's in her late forties and is having hormone therapy, it's probably because she's having a difficult menopause.

'And if she's having a difficult menopause it probably means she's depressed.' He shrugged. 'ETC might even *help* her,' he added with a thin smile.

Lippencott lay back and closed his eyes. 'This is *madness*, Russ. You know that, don't you? Absolute bloody madness!'

Yuncker helped himself to one of Lippencott's panatellas, lit it with Fitzpatrick's lighter and crossed to examine the damage Linda had done to his graph paper. 'Well it's up to you. I can lay on everything except the personnel.' He began to roll up the graph paper.

After a moment or two of uneasy silence, Fitzpatrick – still smarting from the questions he had been asked about Clair – said: 'Mr Yuncker, let me ask *you* a tough question. Just why is it you're so anxious to help?'

But before he had a chance to reply, Lippencott answered for him. 'Because he thinks Pierce might *just* be into something of interest to the CIA. Once a Company man, always a Company man.' He opened his eyes and gave Yuncker a long hard look. 'Right, Russ?'

Yuncker picked up the roll of graph paper and put it back into his briefcase. 'Let's just say I don't like locked-room mysteries,' he replied, apparently in no way offended by what had been said. He began to put on his jacket. 'So, what's it to be?'

'How quickly could you get hold of the gear?' asked Lippencott.

Yuncker poured himself some more of the now tepid coffee. 'In time for Monday morning. Tuesday at the latest . . .'

Lippencott turned to Fitzpatrick. 'How're you fixed? Could you stay over for another day or so?'

'Jesus!' He pulled a long face. 'I've already pushed my luck not filing the Seaquarium story. Still . . .'

'Okay.' Lippencott got up and began to walk towards the door. 'I'll go talk to Linda,' he said. 'If I'm not back in ten minutes call the cops.'

25

On the following Tuesday, Lippencott and Fitzpatrick arrived
at Pierce's apartment block at precisely 7.40 a.m.

Fitzpatrick was carrying a bunch of flowers and a TWA flight
bag he had bought the previous day, and Lippencott a suitcase.

'Good morning, gentlemen!' said the security guard cheerfully. 'Mrs Pierce, is it?'

Lippencott chuckled. 'Now that's what I *call* a good memory!'

'In this job you need it,' the guard replied, pleased with the
compliment. He crossed to the desk and picked up the house
phone. 'She's expecting you, is she?'

'She is.' Fitzpatrick held up the flowers. 'I promised I'd stop
off on my way to the airport to say goodbye.'

The guard nodded understandingly. 'The only reason I asked,' he said, dialling Pierce's number, 'is that I've just sent
someone up to her apartment.'

He put the telephone to his ear. 'There are two gentlemen in
the lobby for Mrs Pierce. A Mr Lippencott and Mr—' He
hesitated, not quite able to remember the name.

'Fitzpatrick.'

'Mr Fitzpatrick. Fine, I'll send them straight up.'

The door to Pierce's apartment was opened by an unsmiling
Linda, who was wearing her nurse's uniform.

'Everything okay, honey?' asked Lippencott.

Without answering she turned, led them through the hall
and down a length of corridor into the master bedroom.

Like the drawing-room, it was opulently furnished. Lying
unconscious on an enormous four-poster, was Pierce. She was
wearing a black négligé trimmed with mink and fluffy black
bedroom slippers.

Lippencott put down the suitcase, and, after taking a quick
look around, removed a vase full of arum lilies and some copies
of *Vogue* from an occasional table and carried it across to the
bed. Then, as Fitzpatrick unzipped his flight bag, he brought
the suitcase over to the table and unlocked it. Inside – carefully

cushioned with tissue paper – was an oxygenator and a face mask, a rubber gag, a pair of electrodes and the ECT machine: a one-foot-square, teak-clad transformer with a time switch for delivering a measured pulse of electricity. After first removing the smaller pieces of equipment, Lippencott lifted the ECT machine out of the case and put it gently down on the table beside the two tape-recorders – one belonging to Yuncker – which Fitzpatrick had taken from his flight bag. Lippencott plugged the ECT machine into a nearby electricity socket and began unwinding the cord from around the electrodes. 'Are you sure she hasn't had breakfast?' he asked Linda, who was busy attaching needles to the nozzles of two 2-millilitre disposable syringes.

'She said she hadn't . . .'

'And you've checked the kitchen?' he asked, plugging the electrodes into the ECT machine.

Linda charged one of the syringes with atrophine, a saliva inhibitor, and held it up to the light to see that it was free from bubbles. 'Of *course* I checked the kitchen,' she replied testily, laying aside the first syringe to charge the second with succinyl-choline, a muscle relaxant.

After putting a finger inside Pierce's mouth to make sure she wasn't wearing dentures, she put the gag between her teeth. Next, she wiped the back of Pierce's left hand with an alcohol sponge, pinched up the soft, pale skin and carefully inserted one needle and then the other. Finally, she placed the electrodes over Pierce's head so that the contact pads rested on either temple, cupped the woman's jaw firmly in her hand and turned to Lippencott. 'Right, now!'

Lippencott pressed a button on the top of the ECT machine, sending a 120-volt charge of electricity through the frontal lobes of the unconscious woman's brain.

In the early days of electroconvulsive therapy, patients thrashed so violently that limb dislocations and fractures were common. But because of the succinylcholine, the only evidence of the electrically induced epileptic fit to which Pierce was being subjected was a slight movement of her neck and facial muscles.

Working even more quickly than before, Linda removed the electrodes and the gag, placed the face mask over Pierce's mouth and nose and began squeezing the oxygenator's ventilating bag.

As soon as she had finished with the oxygenator, Lippencott put it back into the suitcase with the rest of the equipment and took it out into the hall.

When he returned Linda was sitting on the side of the bed chafing Pierce's hands. 'Mrs Pierce?' she called. 'Mrs Pierce, can you hear me?'

By now the colour had come back to her cheeks, and after Linda had repeated her name several more times she blinked and opened her eyes. 'What happened?' she asked in a small, cracked voice.

Linda gave her a sip of water. 'You fainted, just after I'd given you your injection.'

Pierce rolled her head over on the pillow and stared dully up at the two men. 'Why are they here?'

'You asked them to come to see you,' Linda explained. 'Don't you remember? You've something you want to tell them.'

Pierce turned back to Linda, a bewildered expression on her face. 'Something I want to tell them?'

She nodded. 'You want to tell them about Clair – Clair Tennant.'

Linda signalled to Fitzpatrick that now was the time to switch on the tape-recorders.

'Clair Tennant?'

Linda looked into Pierce's face. 'That's right, Clair Tennant. You know Clair Tennant, don't you, Mrs Pierce?'

Pierce closed her eyes and nodded. 'What do you want me to tell you about her?'

While Lippencott was at the front door giving one of Yuncker's men his tape-recorder and the suitcase containing the ECT machine, Fitzpatrick got up and crossed to the bedroom window.

During the past twenty-five minutes Pierce had told them everything they had wanted to know – where Clair was being held, how she had been abducted, why and by whom.

At first he had felt only a burning hatred for Pierce and

Snaith and Mancini, but then, as it became clear that Clair was unharmed, his feelings of relief had been overtaken by the sudden realization that he was sitting on one of the biggest stories of the century.

He knew what he should do – as soon as he had been to the police, he should phone the story in to his own paper.

And yet this would be giving away a fortune. Thoughts of the money he could earn if he were free of any such obligation began to enter his mind. Thoughts of a world exclusive sold to the highest bidder and followed, a few months later, by a book bigger than *Alive* or *All the President's Men*; thoughts of serialization rights, foreign rights, book club rights, paperback rights, even, perhaps, film rights . . .

Of course, with that kind of money he'd have to become a tax exile, but that wouldn't be so bad. He and Clair could buy themselves a house in Ireland, perhaps. In fact Ireland made a lot of sense from every point of view. She'd liked the country when they'd visited his parents at Christmas. And if she wanted to carry on working she could. London, after all, was only an hour's flying time from Dublin, and providing she didn't give up her own UK residentship she could visit it as often as she wished.

All he needed was a few more hours in which to get himself fired and find an agent.

He turned as Lippencott came back into the bedroom and told Linda it was time for her to leave.

'Are you feeling all right?' she asked Pierce, as she began hurriedly packing her nurse's bag. 'Are you sure there's nothing I can get you before I go?'

Pierce smiled weakly. 'No, you've been very kind . . .'

Lippencott returned from seeing Linda to the door with a bemused expression on his face. 'Women!' he said, crossing to the French cradle phone that was standing on one of the bedside tables. He picked up the ornate ivory-and-gold handset and began dialling. 'After what we've come up with this morning, she's still doing her number about ends not justifying the means!'

'Who're you calling?'

'The cops, of course . . .'

162

Fitzpatrick moved quickly across the room and cut him off. 'Look, Ed, do we *have* to call them right now?'

'What do you mean, do we have to call them now? Of course we have to call them now!'

'Wouldn't this evening or tomorrow morning do just as well? I mean, we know Clair's safe . . .' Fitzpatrick ran his fingers through his hair. 'Look, Ed, I don't know how to say this, but – well – I need a little while longer to get everything wrapped up. Just a few more hours, that's all. After all this time, surely to Christ a few more *hours* aren't going to make any difference? And I promise you, it's as much for Clair's sake as my own . . .'

'Mike, I know how you feel,' said Lippencott gently. 'Believe me, I do know how you feel. But listen, man, this isn't a John Wayne movie. You've already done more than anyone could be expected to do, so let the cops handle it from here on in, huh?'

Suddenly Fitzpatrick realized that Lippencott thought he was asking for time in which to rescue Clair and avenge himself on Snaith and Mancini.

A great wave of self-disgust washed over him. 'Sure,' he said, turning away. 'You're right. Go ahead and call them.'

26

Two smartly dressed men got out of the Yellow Cab which had just pulled up in front of the hotel across the avenue from Pierce's apartment block. One was Paul Ginzel and the other Pedro Sanchez. Ginzel was carrying a copy of the *Wall Street Journal*, and Sanchez an expensive-looking black leather document case.

While he waited for Sanchez to pay the driver, Ginzel turned and looked across at the squad cars drawn up in the forecourt of Pierce's block. 'Seems as if they're collecting for the Police Benefit early this year,' he said, slipping the doorman a dollar.

The doorman tipped his cap. 'And they're not taking no for an answer,' he replied, setting the revolving door turning for the two men. 'They've been in there for half an hour already.'

Once through the door, they removed their hats, crossed the busy lobby and took an elevator to the fifth floor. After walking briskly down the corridor on the avenue side of the hotel, they retraced their steps and took another elevator to the sixth floor, where they followed the same procedure. This time, however, they found what they had been looking for – a door with a DO NOT DISTURB notice hanging on it.

After making sure they were alone, each snapped on a pair of surgical gloves and a rubber skull mask, and, as Sanchez slipped the sharp edge of a wooden wedge beneath the door, Ginzel knocked discreetly. 'Bellboy,' he called.

From inside the room a man's voice replied: 'What is it?'

'I've a package marked urgent.'

'Leave it outside.'

After explaining that he was not allowed to do so, Ginzel knocked again.

'Okay, okay!' said the man in an exasperated voice. 'I'm coming, for chrissake . . .'

There was the sound of bolts being withdrawn. Then, as the door began to open, Ginzel kicked the wedge firmly into place.

The man inside tried to slam the door, but with the wedge

jammed between it and the floor, this was no longer possible.

Quick as a flash, Ginzel produced a pair of bolt-cutters from inside his copy of the *Wall Street Journal* and sliced effortlessly through the security chain. As he did so, Sanchez ran at the door with his shoulder, sending the man inside staggering back towards a bed in which a girl with long red hair was lying.

As Ginzel turned the lock behind them, Sanchez drew an automatic from inside his jacket. 'Into the bathroom, both of you!' he snapped.

The man wrapped his bathrobe more tightly around himself and began sidling towards the chair on which his clothes were lying. Beads of sweat had begun to appear on his bald head. 'Now listen, you guys,' he said, trying to sound reasonable and relaxed. 'If it's dough you want—'

Sanchez clicked back the hammer of his automatic. 'You got exactly ten seconds to get your fat ass into the bathroom, or it'll be all over the carpet. Now *move*!'

Reinforced by the sound of the hammer being cocked, the threat had a galvanizing effect on the couple. Clutching a sheet around herself, the girl scrambled down off the bed and made a dash for the bathroom.

As she passed Sanchez, he grabbed hold of a corner of the sheet and tore it away from her; apart from a pair of black stockings and a suspender belt, she was naked.

Chuckling, he followed them through into the bathroom. 'Okay, *amigo*,' he said, tossing the sheet to the man, 'start tearing it into strips.'

Leaving Sanchez to oversee the tying up of the couple, Ginzel pulled off his mask, crossed to the window and lifted one of the slats of the Venetian blind.

Satisfied that nothing had changed on the opposite side of the avenue, he opened Sanchez's document case and took out a glass-cutter, a rubber suction pad, several clips of .45 calibre hollow-point ammunition, a twelve-inch-long silencer and what has been described as the pocket version of the Thompson sub-machine-gun – a squat, grey anodized Ingram MAC 10.

Ten-and-a-half inches long and weighing a mere six-and-a-quarter pounds, the MAC 10 has an effective range of 108 yards and is capable of firing 1,445 rounds a minute. Furthermore, when fitted with its own lightweight sound-suppressor, it does so in almost total silence.

As soon as he had screwed the silencer on to the barrel and pulled out the skeleton stock, he returned to the window and sighted the gun at the entrance to Pierce's apartment block. Laying it aside, he raised the blind six inches, spat on the suction pad and pressed it hard against the window, then began cutting the glass around it.

By the time he had finished, he had been rejoined by Sanchez, who picked up the gun, switched to fire and full automatic, and drew back the milled cocking handle.

'Okay?' asked Ginzel, giving up his seat to allow Sanchez to sight the gun for himself.

'Seems to be just fine.'

Ginzel turned back to the document case and took out a pair of binoculars and a transistor radio. After extending the telescopic aerial, he switched on the radio and put his ear to the speaker.

'What're you doing?' asked Sanchez, glancing over his shoulder.

'We've been kinda worried about Pierce for some time now,' Ginzel explained, as he plugged an earpiece into the radio. 'So, when Fitzpatrick hit town we thought it mightn't be a bad idea if we fitted infinity transmitters into her phones.'

'Infinity transmitters?'

'They pick up anything that's being said in a room, even when the phone's on the hook.' Ginzel paused to make a small adjustment to the aerial, then pressed the earpiece more firmly into place. 'I've got 'em!' he said, looking pleased with himself. 'Got 'em loud 'n'clear!'

'If you could *hear* what was going on, why did it take you so long to call me, for chrissake?'

'It was the Old Man. He took a lot of persuading that this wasn't just dirty pool, but the only thing we *could* do in the circumstances . . .'

Sanchez shook his head. 'Well, he's just fuckin' lucky we got here in time,' he said. 'Anyway, where's he taken his ass off to now?'

'The Old Man?' Ginzel carried the radio across to the bed and made himself comfortable. 'To the island, of course.'

'You know something?' Sanchez continued, almost wistfully. 'I can't help feeling kinda sorry for him. I mean, all the dumb bastard ever did was work, and look where it's got him!'

'How do you mean, look where it's got him?'

'Well, he's finished, isn't he? All washed up. After today he'll be lucky if he can get himself a job shaving patients for surgery.'

Ginzel laughed quietly. 'You're kidding? Listen, he's only just begun! According to Quintrell, in a year they'll be ready to invite independent medical observers to the island to watch the Old Man do his number on a real patient! And once that's happened, Quintrell reckons he's an odds-on favourite for a Nobel Prize!'

'Okay, but with a Federal warrant out on him there's no way he'll ever be able to return to the States.'

'When they get a sniff of some of the things he's been cooking up on the island, they'll find a way of letting bygones be bygones. Like they did with Wernher von Braun. Christ, before he joined NASA, that sonuvabitch had been building rockets which killed thousands of limey civilians during World War II!'

'Sure, but—'

'Hold it!' Ginzel put his fingers to the earpiece and listened intently for a moment. 'I think . . .' He nodded. 'Yes, they're just getting ready to move out!'

Detective Lieutenant Bernard Dougherty – a thick-set man with dark jowls and close-cropped hair – took a dog-eared card from the back pocket of his maroon slacks and began reading Pierce her rights. He had a flat, rasping voice and he read slowly and loudly, as if to someone hard of hearing.

'You understand that?' he asked, when he had come to the end of what was printed on the card.

Pierce – still in her négligé but now sitting on one of the little gilt chairs in the drawing-room – nodded dully, then went back to plucking at the lace handkerchief lying in her lap.

'What we're goin' to do now is take a ride downtown where we'll ask you to make another statement,' Dougherty explained.

'Only this time it'll be in writing. Now, do you wanna call your attorney?'

'Call my attorney?'

'That's right, ma'am. Your attorney. You do *have* an attorney, don't you?'

'I guess so . . .'

'You *guess* so?' After exchanging bewildered glances with the other police officers, Dougherty tried again. 'Mrs Pierce, *please* try to understand,' he said patiently. 'You've a right to an *attorney*. Now, do you want to exercise that right?'

Pierce shrugged, and began humming quietly to herself.

'Just what the hell have you done to this dame?' he asked Lippencott. 'I can't get the time of day out of her . . .'

'She talked to me!' he replied, holding up the cassette that had been used to record her statement. 'But then – let's face it, Bernie – interrogation never was one of your strong points!'

Dougherty snatched the cassette from him and held it in front of Pierce's face. 'Listen, lady, you wanna tell me how these guys got you to tell 'em what's been happenin'?'

'They just asked me . . .' she replied flatly, then went back to her tuneless humming.

'They just asked you!' Dougherty gave up. Turning, he called across to the patrolman standing near the door: 'Tell 'em downstairs that we'll be leavin' in ten minutes.

'And listen,' he added, struggling to re-button the collar of his white short-sleeved shirt, 'I want the lobby and the forecourt clear when we come out, y'heah.'

The patrolman left the room, and, while Dougherty began questioning Lippencott and Fitzpatrick again, a uniformed policewoman took Pierce back into the bedroom where the maid helped her to dress and pack an overnight bag.

As soon as they returned Dougherty stood up, eased his Detective Special in its holster and began pulling on his peppermint-striped jacket.

'Cuffs?' asked one of the plainclothes officers, nodding towards Pierce.

Dougherty shook his head.

After shepherding everyone out on to the landing, Dougherty watched while one of the uniformed officers sealed the doors of the apartment. Leaving the cleaning woman and the maid (who was carrying a cage containing Pierce's cockatoo) to be escorted down by the officer who had sealed the doors, he ushered Pierce, the policewoman, Lippencott and Fitzpatrick into the elevator.

Without speaking, they rode down to the lobby, where still more uniformed policemen were waiting for them.

After marshalling everyone in the middle of the floor, Dougherty put on his sunglasses and went out on to the top of the steps leading down to the forecourt. Reassured that the coast was clear, he turned and beckoned to the others to follow.

Half-way down the flight of steps, Fitzpatrick – who was walking in front of Pierce – felt something fly past his head, followed almost simultaneously by what sounded like a tennis ball being hit by a racquet.

He turned. To his amazement, Pierce seemed to be running up the steps backwards.

A cloud of what looked like red dust materialized in front of him, and he felt something warm and wet splash across his face.

As the cloud diffused and began to drift away on the breeze, he could see that bits of Pierce were flying off in all directions – fingers, teeth, fragments of skull with the hair still attached . .

Although what he was watching could only have been measured in seconds, like a nightmare, it seemed to go on and on for ever.

Out of the corner of his eye he saw the policewoman and one of the plain-clothes officers stagger and begin to fall, and then his attention was taken by the blaring of a car horn from across the avenue.

He turned in time to see a white Chevrolet convertible pull violently away from the curb.

To avoid hitting the convertible, the driver of a two-tone Chrysler Newport that was coming up behind braked hard enough to produce a locked-wheel skid.

There was a screech of tyres, followed by a loud crash and the tinkle of glass as a station wagon ran into the back of the Chrysler. A moment later the station wagon itself was hit from behind by a blue delivery truck.

Pursued by one of the Chrysler's chrome hubcaps, the Chevrolet straightened up and went roaring off down the avenue.

'The Chevvy!' somebody yelled above the blaring of horns. 'The shots came from the white Chevvy!'

With the air now acrid with the smell of burnt powder, Sanchez withdrew the barrel of the MAC 10 from the hole in the window, and, as calmly as if he had been on a firing range, waited for Ginzel to pronounce on the accuracy of his aim.

The tightly packed cluster of expanding bullets had carried Pierce further than Ginzel had expected, and it took him a moment to relocate her.

She was lying spread-eagled on her back, with her face turned to the side. The whole of the back of her head was missing, and through his binoculars he could see that what remained of her skull was as empty as a blown egg.

'Right on the button!' he said, as the first of the squad cars – its siren whooping and its emergency lights flashing – roared off in pursuit of the white Chevrolet. 'Though I still think we should've taken out Fitzpatrick while we were about it . . .'

'*Now* he tells me!' Irritably, Sanchez slammed a new clip of ammunition into the grip and put the gun to his shoulder.

'Don't!' Ginzel lowered his binoculars to give him a hard look. 'The Old Man was adamant it should be a surgical procedure. As it is, he'll be sore as hell when he hears you've winged a brace of cops . . .'

After stripping off their gloves, they wiped their sweating hands on the coverlet, picked up their hats, the empty document case and the *Wall Street Journal* and took one last look out of the window.

Crowds had begun to form on either side of the avenue, and traffic was at a standstill, with many drivers standing on their fenders, craning their necks for a better view. By now, blood from Pierce's body had reached the bottom step and was beginning to form a pool in the forecourt.

Using the handkerchief from his breast pocket, Ginzel withdrew the bolts and they stepped out into the empty corridor, closing the door quietly behind them. Five minutes later, having left the hotel by a rear exit, they were in a taxi on their way to Miami International Airport, $20,000 richer than when they had arrived.

'Well, at least we've got ourselves a warrant,' Dougherty announced, as he entered the interrogation room of the modernistic, brick-and-concrete Police Headquarters Building in down-town Miami. 'Unlawful Flight.'

'*Unlawful Flight*?' Fitzpatrick looked around the smoke-filled room hoping that someone would tell him he had misunderstood. Nobody did.

Dougherty pulled up a chair and sat down. 'It's enough to start extradition proceedings . . .'

'With Snaith's doctors saying he's too ill to return for questioning, extraditing him simply on the strength of Pierce's statement will take forever,' Lippencott pointed out. 'And by then he'll have destroyed the evidence you need to convict him. More important still, what about the girl?'

Dougherty shrugged. 'You should have thought about that before pulling that half-assed stunt to get Pierce to talk.'

Lippencott took out a panatella and reached across the table for Dougherty's book matches. 'And you shouldn't have been so fuckin' incompetent as to let the star witness get blown away!

'Anyway, what about the driver of the Chevrolet? He *must* have been working with the guys who hit Pierce, for chrissake!'

'Uh-huh.' Dougherty lit another cigarette from the one he had been smoking, and ground out the butt on the floor. 'You know that and I know that. But Cahill's story – and he's sticking to it – is that he stopped off at the hotel for a box of cigars, panicked when he saw what was happening across the avenue and just decided to get his ass outta there as fast as he could.

'The way things are going,' he added morosely, 'we'll be lucky if we get him on a dangerous driving rap . . .'

'But Pierce had confessed to having been involved with Snaith in kidnapping and *murder*!' Fitzpatrick insisted. 'She'd told you how the operation worked. She'd named names, dates and places. And all you can do is talk about charging him with failing to return to help the police with their inquiries, or whatever the hell you call it over here? Jesus H. *Christ*!'

Dougherty nodded. 'That's right,' he said grimly. 'And there's something else you'd better know, son.

'Even if Pierce had been properly cautioned before she'd

made her confession – a confession which, I might add, was obtained in violence of the Fourth Amendment – without we come up with *proof* that the crimes charged have been committed, there's no way we're going to be able to get Snaith into court, let alone convict him.'

Fitzpatrick got up and began putting on his jacket.

'Goin' someplace?' asked Dougherty.

'You don't need me any more tonight, do you?'

'That depends on whether you're planning to phone the story in to your paper . . .'

'Is there any reason why I shouldn't?'

'Sorry, but until we know how we're handling this thing, it's gotta stay under wraps.'

Fitzpatrick shook his head. 'You can't do that,' he said, starting towards the door. 'Not in this country, you can't . . .'

'You know something, Bernie?' said one of the FBI officers present. 'These gentlemen are material witnesses, right? Well, don't you think that in the circumstances we ought to provide them with around-the-clock protection?' He winked. 'You know what I mean?'

Fitzpatrick began to protest, but he had not got far before he was interrupted by the telephone. It was for Dougherty.

'It's the DA's office.'

Dougherty swore under his breath. 'Find out what they want, huh?'

The officer who had taken the call did what he'd been asked, then covered the telephone mouthpiece with his hand. 'I think you'd better come and talk to them yourself,' he said. 'Although we have an Extradition Treaty with the Bahamas, they've just discovered we don't have one with Abaco.'

Dougherty twisted around in his seat, frowning. '*Abaco*? What the fuck are they talkin' about?'

The officer held the telephone out to him. 'Hippocrates Cay – the island Snaith's gone to ground in – is part of the Abaco group! *According to the DA's office, we're not going to be able to extradite the sonuvabitch!*'

27

Fitzpatrick was sitting in front of the television, supposedly watching an old James Cagney movie with Lippencott and their FBI guard.

In fact, he was thinking about rescuing Clair. The idea had first occurred to him when he had heard that neither the American nor the British governments had an extradition treaty with Abaco. Then, he had regarded it as little more than a heroic fantasy, but with each day that had passed he had become more and more convinced that if he didn't get her off Hippocrates Cay, nobody would.

Although the Bureau's view was that she was safer now than at any time since her abduction ('There's no way Snaith's going to let anything happen to her,' he had been told, 'she's far too valuable as a hostage.'), Fitzpatrick was not convinced. If no attempt was to be made to arrest Snaith until he made the unlikely mistake of setting foot in a country with whom the US had an extradition treaty, why would he need a hostage?

The *Marlowe* was moored at the end of the garden, there was enough fuel on board to get him to the island, and, although the FBI didn't know it, he was an experienced sailor. So, if he were to slip out of the house in the middle of the night, he could be in Abaconian territorial waters and beyond the reach of the US Coast Guard by the time his absence was noticed. Armed with Lippencott's revolver, he would take Snaith prisoner, force him to release Clair and return to Miami in his helicopter.

It sounded easy enough, except he knew that it would be anything but easy. The waters in which he'd be sailing were among the most treacherous in the world; there were shoals, sandbanks, submerged rocks and bores. And even if he did manage to make a safe and accurate landfall, he'd still have to get past the goddamned plants.

Could the plants really detect stress, or were they – as Lippencott had suggested – only a sophisticated version of the dummy burglar alarm? Although part of him still clung to the belief that plants are little more than senseless automata, the fact that many distinguished scientists believed otherwise made him very uneasy. Eldon Byrd – an operations analyst with the Naval Ordnance Laboratory in Silver Spring, Maryland – had successfully repeated many of Cleve Backster's experiments. So had Ivan Gunar, head of the Department of Plant Physiology at the Timiryazev Academy of Agricultural Sciences in Moscow. So, too, had Marcel Vogel, a research chemist with IBM.

If it was true that plants could detect stress, there was, he knew, no way he was going to get past them – just thinking about it made him sweat.

Yet people did learn to reduce stress – the boom in the sale of transcendental meditation courses and biofeedback machines was evidence of that. However, he had left it too late to take up TM; and even if he could get hold of a biofeedback machine without arousing the suspicions of the FBI, it would require days of practice before he learned to produce alpha waves on demand – weeks or even months before he was able to maintain them in a situation as stressful as the one he would face on Hippocrates Cay.

There was only one thing for it: *if* – and it was a big if – he went to the island, he would have to reduce his stress pharmacologically. Nembutal, he knew, was a drug which depressed the central nervous system. So, providing he didn't allow himself to fall asleep, a couple of 100-milligram capsules taken fifteen minutes before going ashore should free him of all tension and anxiety. The only problem was that it would be at least two hours before he was in a fit state to do anything else. But then he remembered that amphetamine is often given as an antidote to barbiturate poisoning. Like some of his colleagues, he carried Methadrine in case he suddenly found himself with a story which necessitated him working non-stop for forty-eight hours. Supposing, then, he were to take a couple of his uppers once he was beyond the outer perimeter of the plants? In theory, the drugs would cancel one another out; he would neither be sedated nor recklessly high . . .

But wasn't it madness for him to imagine he could carry off something like this single-handed? Reluctantly, he came to the conclusion that it wasn't. In fact, it was probably something

174

only one man *could* do; use more than one, and all you did was increase the likelihood of the alarm being raised.

So, what was it to be? Go, and risk ending up in a corner of a foreign field that is for ever England; or not go?

He decided he would have to go. Or at least get ready to go. There was, after all, always the chance that the authorities would have found a way of rescuing Clair before the time came for him to set sail.

After announcing that he was bored with the movie and was going to bed, he went upstairs, took one of his Methadrine tablets and began plotting a critical path analysis. By breakfast time the next morning he had reduced every phase of the mission to a series of yes/no options, each within its own box and interlinked with arrows.

Next, he would have to devise a method for walking on sand without leaving footprints; discover where Lippencott kept his revolver and ammunition at night; and in order to assuage his conscience, make sure that the *Marlowe* was covered by the appropriate marine insurance. He would have to leave a letter for Lippencott, and another – marked ONLY TO BE FORWARDED IN THE EVENT OF MY DEATH – for his parents. Ideally, he would have liked to make a new will (the one lodged with his solicitors in London had been drawn up before he had met Clair, and in it he had left everything to his parents). However, a new will would have to be witnessed, and that was bound to arouse suspicions. All he could do, therefore, was to ask his parents to settle his account with Lippencott out of the proceeds of his estate, and pass on what remained to Clair if she were to survive him.

Fitzpatrick was a lapsed Catholic, and all this pondering on the possibility of his death had, he discovered, rekindled a spark in the ashes of his faith. For a moment he even wondered whether he shouldn't ask to be taken back into the Church. But he quickly rejected the idea. Whether or not he succeeded was dependent on chance – chance and his ability to go about the task coldly and clinically.

A little before midnight on September 28th, Fitzpatrick let himself quietly out of the house. Draped over his shoulders was

175

an anorak, in the pockets of which were Lippencott's Smith and Wesson and a box of .38 ammunition, and he was carrying a flight bag containing provisions, a knife and a flashlight.

So far, everything had gone smoothly. He had spent that evening as he had spent the past couple of evenings – playing poker with Lippencott and their FBI guard. At 10.45 he had gone into the kitchen, returning several minutes later with three mugs of coffee. The previous night their game had gone on until nearly three in the morning, so no one was surprised when the FBI man began yawning. Not long after, Lippencott had stretched and announced that he, too, was feeling bushed, and would be having an early night.

What neither of them knew was that the coffee they had just drunk contained the contents of eight of Fitzpatrick's 100-milligram Nembutal capsules.

By the time he had changed and was ready to leave, both men were in a deep sleep – Lippencott in bed and the FBI man stretched out in front of the television.

Fitzpatrick made his way across a garden loud with the shrilling of cicadas, and on to the jetty. Although the forecast had talked of scattered thunderstorms, the sky was clear and bright with stars. Once on board, he unlocked the wheelhouse door and switched on the overhead amber lights. The layout was much as he remembered it: behind the wheel was an instrument panel containing oil-pressure, temperature and fuel gauges, a voltmeter, tachometer and ammeter. As well as a compass, there was a direction-finder, an echo-sounder and an electro-magnetic log. To the left of the wheel was a chart table; to the right a twelve-channel marine radio and a cupboard containing, among other things, a set of signal flags, a signalling lamp and a box of distress flares. Hanging above the bench were several bib-type lifejackets, labelled: Designed to turn unconscious wearer face up in the water.

After stowing his belongings, he opened the drawer beneath the chart table and took out a parallel rule, dividers, pencils, an eraser, tide tables and four navigation charts, and settled down to plot his course.

Providing he did not exceed the speed limit and kept within the buoys marking the main channel, getting out of the harbour seemed to present few problems. For most of the time he would be sailing parallel with MacArthur Causeway, and once through Government Cut all he had to do was keep between the buoys marking Bar Cut and Outer Bar Cut and he would be on the correct heading for his next seamark, the lighthouse on Great Isaac – the most northerly of the islands encompassing the Great Bahama Bank. Except it wasn't going to be that easy; the *Cape Canaveral to Key West* chart warned of a magnetic anomaly of three to six degrees in the area between Jupiter Inlet and Molasses Reef, and there would be the two to three-and-a-half knots northerly flowing Gulf Stream to contend with. After making the necessary calculations, he turned to the *Bahama and Abaco Islands* chart. With Great Isaac abaft of him, he would alter course, sail along the Northwest Providence Channel and round the southern tip of Great Abaco. According to his estimate, he should arrive at Hole in the Wall Anchorage at around 2.30 the following afternoon. There he would eat, test-fire Lippencott's gun, and sleep until sunset, when he would set out on the final leg of his voyage, arriving at Hippocrates Cay at a little after midnight.

Plotting his course had taken him longer than he had expected. Instead of carrying out a Basin check, he decided to get under way immediately.

He went back on deck and cast off the headrope, sternrope and springs. With having to double as helmsman and crew, coiling and stowing the mooring ropes and taking in the fenders was something he would have to leave until later.

Hurrying back to the wheelhouse, he switched on the navigation lights and pressed the starter button. Hoping to God he wouldn't wake the men in the house, he throttled back, eased the gearshift into forward drive and edged the vessel gently away from the jetty.

Part Two

Ultimately, all law dissolves into administrative discretion.
Wolfgang Friedmann, *Law in a Changing Society*

28

Madge Forrestal had heard the story before. So, when her husband had begun telling it again, this time for the benefit of the President and First Lady, she had allowed her attention to wander.

They were in the small blue-and-white dining-room in the east wing of the White House. It was a room which Madge Forrestal had always liked, with its magnificent eighteenth-century crystal chandelier and wallpaper depicting scenes from the American Revolution, and – if everything worked out – she intended to keep it much as it was now. She was less certain, however, about the room in which they'd had drinks before dinner. That, she felt, would be improved by moving the Cézanne from the Yellow Oval Room and replacing the brown drapes with ones of the same shade of green as in the painting.

'Good God!' exclaimed the President, brushing his grey hair back from his forehead. 'You really mean that this guy Snaith's been murdering people for their *organs*? In *Miami*?'

Forrestal nodded. 'And it's not just Snaith – some of this country's leading surgeons are implicated,' he replied, in his flat New England accent.

In a recent movie, the part of Forrestal had been played by Robert Redford. It had generally been acknowledged as an excellent piece of casting, for not only did the Attorney-General have the same boyish good looks as the actor, he also had his relaxed manner and easy charm.

'You're kidding?' said the President.

'I'm not. Snaith's a heart surgeon, so, when he had a patient who needed a kidney transplant he'd call in one of the top men in the renal field to perform the actual operation. The same with the liver, or the—'

'Hold it! Are you suggesting that these guys were in on the racket with Snaith?' asked the President, suddenly beginning to look worried.

'No I'm not. That was what was so clever about his set-up – there was never any need for them to know. As far as they were concerned they were doing nothing different from what they did every week of the year – transplanting a well-matched organ from a brain-dead donor in accordance with the customary standards and protocols of medical practice.'

'Darling, *please*!' said the First Lady, wrinkling her nose at the President. 'Do we really have to go on talking about this over dinner?'

Madge Forrestal snapped out of her reverie. 'I'm afraid it's all Hank's fault,' she said, pretending to look disapprovingly at her husband. 'He shouldn't have begun the story in the first place.'

The President smiled sympathetically, but there was still more he wanted to know. 'What about Mancini? Has he had his transplant yet?'

Forrestal shook his head. 'After what's happened, Snaith would have to be crazy to go ahead with it.'

The President's smile faded a little. 'Pity. We might've been able to nail the sonuvabitch for Conspiracy to Murder.'

'We still may.' Forrestal lifted a forkful of rare roast beef to his mouth. 'The trick'll be proving that Mancini *knew* how Snaith had been obtaining his organs.'

'And what about Tennant's boyfriend?' asked the President. 'What's become of him?'

'Fitzpatrick?' Forrestal pulled a long face. 'We're not really sure. Yesterday morning, the *Marlowe* was found abandoned some sixty miles or so northwest of Grand Bahama . . .'

'Oh, no!' exclaimed the First Lady, putting her table napkin to her lips. 'Oh, the poor *man*!'

The President tut-tutted. 'How experienced a sailor was he?' he asked Forrestal.

'Apparently *very* experienced . . .'

'Even so,' said the President, remembering his own days in the Navy, 'I sure wouldn't have liked to sail single-handed into *those* waters . . .'

'What do they think happened to him?' the First Lady asked Forrestal.

'We don't know. The boat was undamaged, and nothing was missing – including Lippencott's gun and the dinghy. There was no sign of a struggle, no bloodstains – nothing.

'The Miami papers, of course, are running it as another Bermuda Triangle mystery . . .'

The President smiled. 'Of course!' he said, pouring more wine. 'I can see the headlines now: Reporter in *Marie Celeste* Riddle!'

'As a matter of fact, I think one of them carried exactly that headline!' said Forrestal, raising his glass to savour the fruity bouquet. He regarded himself as something of a connoisseur of fine wines, and the claret the President had served was, for a man who rarely drank, surprisingly good.

'Oh dear, I *am* sorry,' said the First Lady. 'It was such a romantic thing to have done . . .'

'Romantic, but dumb,' said the President. 'Very dumb.'

'Even so . . .' The First Lady seemed genuinely moved. 'But what do you *think* might have happened to him?' she asked Forrestal.

'He was probably on deck without a safety line, slipped and fell overboard,' said the President, before he had a chance to reply. 'If the *Marlowe* was under power at the time—' He shrugged hopelessly.

'Maybe,' said Forrestal. He picked up his knife and fork and began eating again. 'I'm just not sure . . .'

The President looked amused. 'Oh, c'mon Hank, you're not telling me that *you* believe he was snatched by a giant octopus?'

'Giant octopuses are very passé! Nowadays, it's *always* flying saucers!'

A ripple of uneasy laughter went round the table.

'No, it's beginning to look as if Fitzpatrick might have got ashore,' Forrestal continued, more seriously. 'We've been talking to a patient who's just returned from the island, and according to him someone *did* try to take Snaith on Sunday night. Apparently there was a lot of coming and going, and then the helicopter was started up. Shots were heard, and next morning there were traces of what looked like bloodstains on the helipad. Which is about as much as we know at the moment.

'Oh, except Snaith wasn't seen for a couple of days after the incident,' he added. 'When he did finally reappear, one side of his face was badly bruised and he was walking with a limp. The

182

story *he* put out was that he'd fallen down the stairs in the laboratory . . .'

'Ah, well,' said the President philosophically. He took a sip of wine. 'So, when do you expect to extradite him?'

'*Extradite* him?' Forestal frowned. 'We're not going to be able to extradite him. I thought you understood that?'

The President looked dumbfounded. 'No, I most certainly did *not*! Why aren't we going to be able to extradite him?'

'Don't you remember me saying earlier, Mr President, that Abaco's the island that declared a UDI a couple of years back? That in itself wouldn't necessarily be a problem, except that so far none of the major powers have recognized Abaco as an independent state, including the United States. We've tried serving extradition papers on the Bahamian Government, but I'm afraid they just don't want to know.'

'Hell!' The President began plucking at the loose skin under his chin. 'Has anyone thought of talking to the Minister of State and Commonwealth Affairs? After all, Fitzpatrick and Tennant *are* British subjects. Maybe the Minister would be prepared to put pressure on the Bahamian Government?'

'It's been tried,' Forrestal replied. 'And it got us nowhere. As far as the Bahamians are concerned, trying to enforce an extradition treaty that Abaco says it's no longer a party to is politically far too hot a potato . . .'

The President flung his napkin on the table. 'For God's sake, Hank, why didn't you tell me all this before? When this story breaks, popular support for the Firearms Control Bill will take a nose-dive.'

'What's been happening in Miami has nothing whatsoever to do with the Bill!' replied Forrestal, laughing.

The President looked indignant. 'What do you mean, it's nothing to do with the Bill?' he demanded. 'It's got *everything* to do with the Bill! We've been telling the people of this country that with a professionalized, more highly-integrated police force they won't be needing their guns any more. Turn them over to us, we've been telling them, and America will be a safer and more civilized place in which to live. And then, just as they are coming around to thinking that maybe there's something

183

in what we've been saying, they find out that one of the most viciously criminal rip-offs *ever* has been going on right under our noses, and that there's not a damn thing we can do about it!'

'Oh, come *on*!' Forrestal's eyes glistened behind his blue contact lenses. 'Even if every man, woman and child in the United States were armed to the teeth, it wouldn't have prevented Snaith from doing what he did, *and* getting away with it!'

The President's face darkened. 'That's as maybe. But just try telling that to the guys in the boonies after the Gun Lobby has finished laying *this* story on them. Hank, this is a foul-up, and if you don't know it you should!'

With the atmosphere in the room now buzzing like an overloaded electric circuit, the First Lady decided the time had come for her to try to take some of the heat out of the situation. 'Tell me, Hank, if this man Snaith is living on Abaco, why haven't you served the extradition papers on the *Abaconians*?' she asked, smiling sweetly.

The President nodded. It was a good question and he wished he had thought of it. 'That's right,' he said. 'Surely there's no rule of international law which prevents states from extraditing in the *absence* of a treaty?'

'No, there isn't,' Forrestal replied. 'But the fear of inadvertently recognizing an *un*recognized government is something that worries the hell out of diplomats, and the State Department thinks we may be compromising ourselves if we make a formal approach to the authorities on Abaco.'

'In what way would you be compromising yourselves?' asked the First Lady.

Forrestal thought for a moment. 'I can best explain that with a story about something which happened during World War II,' he said. 'General de Gaulle decided he'd like to send Roosevelt a present of a gorilla from French Equatorial Africa. State got very uptight when they heard the news, because at that time we hadn't recognized de Gaulle's government-in-exile. They thought that accepting the gift might have constituted implied recognition. On the other hand, they knew that the General would've been deeply offended if they'd refused his gift. Fortunately, the gorilla solved the problem for them by dying on its way over.'

'How *sad!*' said Madge Forrestal, completely missing the point of her husband's story.

'Traditionally, states make a practice of not recognizing a secessionary movement – like the one on Abaco – until it's become firmly established,' Forrestal continued. 'For instance, no country recognized the independence of the Southern States during the American Civil War . . .'

He broke off as waiters appeared and began clearing the table for the next course.

'Ah, good!' said the First Lady. 'Dessert. I hope everyone likes Pecan Pie?'

The butler leaned forward and whispered something in her ear. 'Oh!' she said. 'Apparently it's not Pecan Pie, it's Orange Cake . . .'

'I'm sorry, Hank,' said the President, suddenly repentant. 'But we've just got to find a way of getting that sonuvabitch Snaith in front of a Grand Jury, and fast.'

Forrestal sighed. 'You're right. I know you're right. But—' he shrugged '—until he makes the mistake of setting foot in a country with whom we have an extradition treaty, I don't know how we're going to do it . . .'

The President began eating moodily. 'Hank, remind me,' he said, bringing to an end the heavy silence which had settled over the dinner table, 'how did Israel get Adolf Eichman out of Argentina?'

Forrestal exchanged questioning looks with the First Lady. 'They – they abducted him,' he replied warily. 'But Mr President—'

'Hold it a minute, Hank,' he said, his eyes still fixed on his plate. 'So, what happened then?' He waved his spoon. 'I mean, *after* they'd abducted him?'

'Well, it's a long time ago now,' Forrestal began, choosing his words carefully, 'but if my memory serves me right, Argentina demanded the return of Eichman, and Israel refused. So, the matter was referred to the UN Security Council who requested Israel – and I think I'm quoting correctly – "to proceed to an adequate reparation in accordance with the Charter of the United Nations and the rules of international law".'

'But they didn't, did they?' said the President.

Forrestal shook his head. 'The Israeli story was that Eichman had agreed to leave of his own free will. And anyway, it wasn't clear whether the guys who'd seized him were private citizens acting on their own initiative, or with the connivance of the Israeli Government. The fact of the matter, of course, was that they were members of the Israeli Security Services . . .'

'Of course!' said the President, with a stony smile.

'Anyway, the upshot of it all was that the two governments issued a statement simply saying that they regarded the incident as closed. As you know, Eichman was never returned, neither was any form of reparation made.'

The President pushed aside his plate and hooked an arm over the back of his chair. 'Which proves you *can* make an illegal seizure and get away with it,' he announced, looking pleased with himself.

'Mr President,' said Forrestal, shaking his head gravely, 'if you're thinking what I *think* you're thinking, forget it! The arrest of a fugitive criminal by officials of one state in the territory of another is *prima facie* a breach of international law.'

'Okay, but am I not right in thinking that an American court will exercise jurisdiction over a person brought before it, even in violation of international law?' asked the President.

'I'm pretty sure that *US versus Insull* is authority for the view that it will, but that's something I'd have to check out,' replied Forrestal, unhappily. 'Another thing I'd have to check out is whether a person seized illegally has a right of action against those responsible for his unlawful arrest and detention.

'Sorry not to be able to give you the answers off the cuff, but international law's more the Solicitor-General's bag than mine.'

'Fine!' said the President, bringing the conversation to an abrupt end. He pushed back his chair and stood up. 'Now, shall we move next door for coffee?'

'Goddammit, I think it worked!' cried Forrestal, slapping the driving wheel of his coffee-coloured Rolls Royce Camargue. He reached out for his wife's hand and gripped it tightly. 'Y'know, I *really* think it worked!'

'Oh boy!' she said, as if she had been holding her breath since leaving the White House. Wearily, she rolled her head over to look at her husband. 'You know, honey, sometimes I think you enjoy being devious just for the sake of being *devious*. Why couldn't you have come right out with it and *told* him that without you bring in Snaith, you'll be running for office without an issue?'

'For three reasons. One: he actually believes all that crap about him being Mr Clean. So, although we both know what the Firearms Control Bill is *really* about – having me take over from him – it must never, ever be spelt out. Not in so many words.

'Two: for him to get behind something as horny as illegal seizure, he's got to be like *inspired* – y'know what I mean?'

Madge Forrestal lit a cigarette for him and another for herself. 'And the Lord spoke unto Moses, saying: Vex the Midianites, and smite them . . .'

'*Exactly!*'

'And the third reason?' she asked, snuggling down into her palomino mink.

'The third reason's that it just *might* turn sour on us, and if it does I want it on record that I was neither the proponent nor a supporter of the idea.

'However,' he added, 'I don't see why it should, in which case I'll still have myself one hell of an issue with which to run, he'll go out with his popularity at an all-time high, making his endorsement of my candidacy gold-plated, which can't be bad!'

While they were waiting for the lights to change at the intersection of 19th Street and Pennsylvania Avenue, Forrestal turned and snapped open the lid of his document case. 'Here,' he said, handing his wife a file marked PERSONAL FOR ATTORNEY-GENERAL'S EYES ONLY. 'Take a look at that.'

She switched on the map light and opened the file. 'Is this what I *think* it is?'

Forrestal nodded. 'Hippocrates Cay. I had the Bureau's

office in Miami fly a photo-reconnaissance mission over the island yesterday.'

She held the photograph closer to the light. 'What're all these yellow marks?'

'Those, my darling,' he replied as he accelerated away, 'those are possible landing sites for a task force!'

29

Things began to happen more quickly than the Attorney-General had expected.

He had just stepped out of the shower the following morning when a call had come through on his bathroom telephone.

It had been the President. 'Say, listen,' he'd begun. 'I've been awake most of the night mulling over what we were talking about last evening. Hank, do you know what I think we should do?'

'Do?' Forrestal had managed to sound genuinely puzzled. 'About what?'

'About this Snaith business, goddammit! I think we should go in there and get the sonuvabitch!'

At the start, most of the President's advisers had been opposed to the idea of an illegal seizure, with Forrestal urging that it should be the last, not the first option to be explored.

But as one alternative after another had been examined and rejected, resistance to the idea of an illegal seizure had crumbled. As the President had said on the evening he had finally swung the consensus his way: 'Why the hell should it *only* be the Israelis who can get away with a number like this?'

The decision to make the seizure had been followed by protracted discussions. How was it to be made? And by whom? Some thought a SWAT squad should be used; others, led by the Director of the CIA, thought it better that it be carried out by private citizens, preferably recruited from within Abaco itself.

Finally, however, the President had approved the most conventional of the plans laid before him. At dawn on October 31st (with his usual flair for what makes a good headline, he had insisted on the mission being moved back forty-eight hours to coincide with Hallowe'en), the destroyer *Holt* would put ashore an assault squad composed of men picked from the 1st Ranger Battalion.

Code-named Operation Witch-finder, it was to be a limited,

low-level action using the absolute minimum of force. As the President had said to Major-General Mark Ackland, the Vietnam veteran who would lead the assault: 'Remember, you're not there to kill gooks. This is a police action and I want it to look like it. So, there's to be no tiger suits and no helmet graffiti.'

The Rangers would secure the island, liberate Clair Tennant, and, to use a phrase which had been coined for the official press release, 'persuade Dr Snaith and certain of his associates to return to the mainland to assist Federal and State law-enforcement officers with their enquiries'.

Using aerial photographs and other intelligence data, a full-size mock-up of Hippocrates Cay had been hastily built in Fort Stewart, Georgia. There, with naval officers in attendance, the Rangers had begun rehearsing their seizure of the island.

Meanwhile, equally painstaking preparations were being made in Washington to deal with the possible legal and diplomatic consequences of such a seizure. US ambassadors had been briefed, and a drafting committee had begun work on an explanatory address to the nation that the President would broadcast early in the evening of Hallowe'en.

And then, with five days to go to D-Day, fate had intervened to deal the President's plan a totally unexpected blow.

Hurricane Hilda had begun her life innocently enough, as little more than a weak tropical depression centred to the west of the Cape Verde Islands.

But the depression had become charged with warm, moist air which had begun to rise through the atmosphere like an enormous bubble. As it did so, it had been replaced by an inflow of cooler air, which, in turn, had become warm and saturated.

It had not been long before the rotation of the earth about its axis had set this now continuous stream of ascending air slowly revolving in an anti-clockwise direction. The higher the air rose, the cooler it became, until finally it had reached its dewpoint. Clouds had begun to mass and there had been thunderstorms and torrential rain. Latent energy far in excess of that released by a thermo-nuclear explosion had thrust the air still higher and caused it to revolve even faster. The clouds had lowered dramatically and had been drawn out along the wind like enormous black curtains, spiralling inwards towards the core of the storm.

Soon, the wind had been revolving so fast that it had flown away from its own centre, like clothes in a spin-dryer. Now 300 miles wide, Hilda had grown an *eye*: a fifteen-mile-wide, ten-mile-high funnel of spinning cloud enclosing an area which had suddenly become eerily still and sunny. So low was the atmospheric pressure within the eye, that the ocean had been sucked up into it, several feet above normal.

Fully mature and travelling at a speed of twelve miles an hour, Hilda had begun to move westwards towards the Americas.

She was first spotted by a weather surveillance satellite on October 12th, and an advisory had been teletyped from the National Hurricane Center to Weather Service stations at Miami and San Juan. By October 14th, Hilda had moved far enough west for specially equipped C-130 reconnaissance aircraft to be sent out to probe her. Based on their findings, a hurricane watch had been issued in San Juan, followed, twenty-four hours later, by a hurricane warning. A massive evacuation of the more vulnerable of the Windward and Leeward Islands had been set in motion, and Red Cross emergency shelters had been opened.

Hilda had made her first landfall thirty-six hours later on the island of Barbados. As the barometer fell, squalls began hitting the island in rapid succession. The wind had increased until it was a solid roar, bringing with it a tumbling storm tide eighteen feet above normal. Before anemometers had been blown away, wind speeds of 190 miles an hour were recorded. Trees had been uprooted, vehicles swept from roads and buildings levelled. And by the time Hilda had moved out into the Caribbean, 600 million gallons of rain-water had poured down upon every square mile of the chain of battered islands.

The path Hilda was expected to follow would have taken her to the south of Jamaica, up through the Straits of Yucatan and into the Gulf of Mexico, which she would have continued until she ran aground somewhere in the region of Galveston, Texas. Instead, at round about latitude 15°N, longitude 70°W, she

191

had begun to swing north. Ahead of her lay the island of Haiti, and beyond the Bahamas.

Forrestal heard the news about Hilda from a duty officer at the State Department as he was about to begin dinner in his brick-and-shingle house in Georgetown. Five minutes after taking the call he was at the wheel of his car, heading for Foggy Bottom.

There had been a lot of argument about where the command centre for Operation Witch-finder should be located. Aware that Witch-finder might backfire in their faces, most of the participants were anxious not to be identified with it *too* closely. The Secretary of State, for example, had argued that the command post should be either in the Pentagon or across the Potomac in the National Military Command Center. But the Secretary of Defense had pointed out that since Witch-finder was a police rather than a military action it should be run from within the Department of Justice – a suggestion which Forrestal had opposed vigorously, saying that Justice had neither the space nor the facilities for such a post.

In the end the President had ruled that it was to be run from within the State Department, because it was State which would have to bear the brunt of any repercussions following the mission, and anyway it already had one of the best command posts in Washington.

Set up in 1961, the Operations Center is a vast clearing-house for information, manned twenty-four hours a day, seven days a week. Intelligence reports and every cable categorized as Immediate or Flash sent from all American embassies, consulates and legations come into it, and it is here that key military and diplomatic personnel assemble during times of international crisis.

The traffic was heavy, and it took Forrestal longer than he had expected to drive to the State Department Building. To avoid the risk of being seen by members of the press, he entered the building from the rear and took a freight elevator to the seventh floor.

Once out of the elevator, he hurried down a now familiar passageway to the door of the Operations Center, where a guard in a bullet-proof booth handed him a pink visitor's badge and rang through to announce his arrival.

The door was unlocked by a man Forrestal recognized as one of the assistant duty officers, and he was led into the Center's main conference room.

The room was crowded. The President was there, standing at the head of a long mahogany table on which was a scale model of Hippocrates Cay. With him was the Secretary of Defense, the Chairman of the Joint Chiefs of Staff, and a young naval officer carrying a large black portfolio.

Forrestal had just begun to make his way through the crowd to speak to the chief duty officer, when the President called the assembly to order.

'Okay,' he said, as soon as he had everyone's attention. 'First let me apologize for having had to call you back after what I'm sure has already been a long and tiring day. However, as some of you already know, we've got a problem. Just like a woman, Hurricane Hilda has decided to go in a different direction from the one expected. All the indications suggest that in less than forty hours she's expected to score a direct hit on Abaco!'

The President held up his hands for silence. 'First I'm going to ask Lieutenant Kellerman here—' he turned towards the naval officer he had been talking with earlier '—to fill you in on the details. Lieutenant Kellerman, as most of you know, is Weather Officer on Witch-finder. After that we'll have to decide just what we're going to do about it.

'If anyone has any questions, the Lieutenant and his colleague from the National Hurricane Research Laboratory will be glad to answer them as we go along.'

Kellerman was tall and painfully thin, with crew-cut red hair and a smooth, boyish face covered with freckles. He was wearing a pair of rimless spectacles which he was constantly having to push back on to the bridge of his nose, and when he walked his shoes squeaked.

Flushed with embarrassment, Kellerman crossed to the head of the table, laid down his portfolio, and began speaking.

Immediately, a voice from the back of the room yelled: 'We can't hear!'

Kellerman cleared his throat. 'Is that better?' he asked, before beginning to explain why he and his fellow meteorologists had, as he put it, 'goofed up on where Hilda was heading'.

As soon as he had finished his ten-minute-long introduction he untied the tapes of his portfolio, took out a map of the Caribbean and held it up for everyone to see.

'Right now Hilda is here,' he explained, pointing to a cluster of tightly packed isobars centred just below the island of Haiti. 'She's moving nor'nor'west at approximately thirteen knots, so by eighteen hundred hours tomorrow—' awkwardly, he put aside the first map and held up another, this time showing Hilda lying over the eastern tip of Cuba '—she'll have moved up to here.

'Now the problem is that once she begins edging out into the Old Bahama Channel we can expect storm swells as far north as Abaco. According to our estimates, an amphibious landing on Hippocrates Cay will become extremely hazardous – maybe even impossible – after eighteen hundred tomorrow.'

'Can we get in ahead of her?' asked the President.

A scar-faced admiral answered for Kellerman. 'Even if we could get everything together by dawn tomorrow, it would take us something like eight hours to steam from Charleston to the Little Bahama Bank. And when we got there the tide as well as the weather would be against us.'

'Why don't we simply postpone until Hilda's come and gone?' asked the Secretary of State.

The President looked enquiringly at Kellerman.

'If you delay, you'll have to delay for at least six, probably ten days,' he explained. 'The problem is—'

'Too long,' said the President. 'Ten days is too long.'

With so many people now involved, security had become his major worry. Treachery aside, one unguarded word to the wrong person at the wrong time would blow the story wide open.

He turned to the man from the National Hurricane Research Laboratory. 'Dr Donahue, what are the chances of us nudging her to one side?' he asked. 'Just enough to miss the Bahamas.'

'You mean by seeding her with silver iodine?' asked Donahue, a florid, white-haired man with a walking stick.

'Now just a *minute*!' said the Secretary of State indignantly.

'Mr President, I'm sorry, but we're still being bugged by Fifi . . .'

'*Bugged*? I don't understand.'

The Deputy Director of the CIA cleared his throat nervously. 'I'm not sure that this is – well— that this is *quite* the time or the place to—'

'Hold it!' said the President. He turned back to the Secretary of State. 'If you've got something to say, say it!'

'I don't know if you remember, but back in 1974, Hurricane Fifi – which was heading towards Miami – suddenly changed course and hit Honduras, killing 10,000 people. Well, a geophysicist at the University of Mexico claims he has evidence that the guys on Project Stormfury were responsible for her changing course. He says we did it to save Miami!'

'That's *ridiculous*!' snapped Donahue. 'Stormfury hasn't seeded a hurricane since Ginger in '71!'

The Secretary of State shrugged. 'Maybe, but the point is that if we get caught horsing around with Hilda, we're in big trouble. Big, *big* trouble! Hell, we're still getting a bad press for Popeye and Rolling Thunder!'

'Okay! *All right*!' Wishing he had never raised the matter, the President moved down the table to look at the model of Hippocrates Cay. 'So, what about air-lifting General Ackland and his men in at dawn tomorrow? Put him down on the helipad,' he said, rapping the white plaster disc at the southern end of the island with his knuckle. 'You could be ready by dawn tomorrow, couldn't you, General?'

Ackland thought about it for a moment. He was tall, broad-shouldered and had a strong, lean face and close-cropped hair that was beginning to grey at the temples. Beneath his combat infantry badge and jump wings he wore the ribbons of the Congressional Medal of Honor, the Distinguished Service Cross, the Silver Star, and the Purple Heart.

'I figure we could,' he replied in a soft, Southern drawl. 'It would mean flying my guys in from Savannah, but we could be ready to go by zero six hundred.' He turned to Kellerman. 'What's the met forecast for tomorrow?'

'It's not good – not for a chopper landing. We're expecting gale-force winds in that area well before dawn.'

Ackland pulled a long face. 'Well, I guess that's that . . .'

The President, however, was not giving up so easily. 'Why does it have to be by chopper? Why can't we have a fixed-wing aircraft land right here on the lawn?' he asked, pointing at the rectangle of green in front of the hospital.

Nobody spoke.

'Well, what about it?'

A USAF general eased his way through to the table, slipped on a pair of horn-rimmed spectacles and stared down at the model. 'What scale is this thing supposed to be?'

Nobody seemed certain.

'For crying out loud!' said the President. 'Someone must know! Where's the guy who built it?'

The chief duty officer hurried across to one of the phones at the back of the room and dialled a number. 'It's a quarter of an inch to a foot,' he called out a moment later.

The USAF general shook his head hopelessly. 'I don't see how it can be done, Mr President. Not with these trees to the north of the lawn and the laboratory building to the south.'

The chief duty officer came back to the table and handed the general a ruler.

'Two hundred and sixty by a hundred and twenty metres, as near as dammit,' he said, after he had finished measuring the model lawn. 'It *definitely* can't be done. No way!'

'Not even with a STOL transport?' asked the President.

'Not even with a STOL transport. If it scraped off paint getting in over the top of the trees, there *still* wouldn't be enough runway left for it to avoid running smack into the lab building. And you'd be in almost as much trouble if you came in over the lab, even though it's not as high as the trees.

'Mind you,' he added. 'I guess we could always try taking out the trees. Have a Phantom lay down a few H and E shells and a little napalm just before the transport shows up . . .'

'No!' said the President, sternly. 'I thought I'd made it clear from the outset that we must accomplish our objectives with the absolute minimum amount of force and destruction of property.'

The general looked at him over the top of his glasses. 'But I'm only suggesting we fell a few *trees*,' he said in a hurt voice.

'What happens if we miss the trees and hit the goddamned hospital?'

The Chairman of the Joint Chiefs of Staff took his pipe from his mouth and looked around the room. 'Now let's hold our horses for a minute, gentlemen,' he said. 'If *we* know Hilda's heading for Hippocrates Cay, so must Snaith. So how come we're so sure he'll still be there when we arrive?

'If I were Snaith I know what I'd be doing right now – I'd be high-tailing it off that island faster than a frog can lick fleas!'

'It's not going to be so easy for him to do that,' Forrestal pointed out. 'He's not going to be able to fly out – Abaco doesn't have an international airport. And if he tries to slip out through Freeport or Nassau he'll be picked up just like *that*!' he said, snapping his fingers.

'So he goes by sea!'

'No way!' Forrestal insisted. 'The only places within range of his yacht with whom we don't have extradiction treaties are Cuba and Haiti, and he'd have to be out of his mind to try that with Hilda moving up the Bahama Channel!'

'What about his patients?' somebody asked. 'Surely he's going to have to evacuate them, isn't he?'

'I've just heard they're arriving in Miami right now,' said an Assistant Director of the FBI who had been called away to the phone a couple of minutes earlier. 'Incidentally,' he added, 'we've pulled Mancini in for questioning, though I don't know how much longer we're going to be able to hold him. The son-avabitch has got himself a whole mess of lawyers, all screaming habeas corpus!'

Ackland turned to Dr Donahue. 'Tell me, just what sort of shape is this place going to be in after Hilda's scored a direct hit?' he asked, nodding at the model.

'Jelesnianski's storm surge model suggests it'll be swept clean.'

'When you say it'll be swept clean, do you really mean it?'

'The laboratory will probably survive, if I'm right in assuming it has a reinforced concrete frame—'

'It has,' said Ackland. 'And what about these?' He pointed to the trees at the north end of the lawn.

Donahue smiled indulgently. 'They'll be matchwood even before the eye gets to them.'

'Now what *about* this eye?'

Donahue looked puzzled. 'What about it?'

Ackland glanced at Kellerman. 'The Lieutenant here was saying earlier that it's fifteen miles wide, and is expected to pass right over the island. Do you go along with his estimate?'

Donahue nodded cautiously, as though he sensed he was being led into some sort of trap.

'And the eye is *completely* calm? No winds, rain – nothing?'

'There'll be some downdraughts, but they should be pretty light.'

'And how long is it likely to be over the island?'

'I should think about an hour or so . . .'

'An hour or so . . .' Ackland considered the implications. 'Okay, we know it's possible to fly reconnaissance missions into hurricanes – the Lieutenant has already told us about the ones flown into Hilda.

'So, what's to stop *us* flying in when the eye's over Hippocrates Cay? With the trees gone and no wind, we should have no problem landing. Also, the local muscle won't be in very good shape for a fight having been worked over by Hilda.'

The President gave him one of his toothy smiles. 'General, it's an interesting idea. But as I'm sure Dr Donahue is about to tell us, you still won't be able to land because the lawn will be covered with debris . . .'

Donahue nodded. 'And rain-sodden,' he added.

'I realize that, Mr President,' said Ackland. 'But what I have in mind is to go in by parachute, get what we came for and clear the lawn so that the aircraft can lift us out.'

The President raised his eyebrows approvingly. 'Sounds like a good idea – a helluva good idea!' He looked around the room to see if anyone would disagree with him. No one did.

'Well, General, it seems we're in business . . .'

Donahue looked dumbfounded. 'But Mr President, flying an aircraft through into the eye of a hurricane is a highly specialized business!'

Ackland took his cap from under his arm and got ready to leave. 'So, we get ourselves a specialist!'

30

Robert Cantrel ducked under the nose of the floodlit DHC-5 Buffalo that had just been rolled out of a hangar into the drizzle at Homestead Air Force Base, and yanked open the cockpit-access hatch.

In spite of having logged a record number of hours flying weather reconnaissance missions into hurricanes, Cantrel – a plump, middle-aged USAF colonel with a mop of black hair and a Zapata moustache – had at first been passed over for Witch-finder on account of his age. But the younger pilots who had been approached had all declined to volunteer. It was one thing, they had said, to fly through a hurricane, quite another to attempt to land and take off in the middle of one, particularly on a makeshift grass runway and in a combat zone.

Cantrel, however, had no such reservations. 'Sure I'll do it,' he had said, 'so long as the money's right and I get to choose the plane and crew.'

Taking a deep breath, Cantrel heaved himself up into the cockpit, threw aside his oilskin and sat down in the left-hand pilot's seat. After stowing the maps, photographs and navigation instruments he had been carrying, he adjusted his seat and rudder pedals and put on a headset.

The flight plan he had prepared would take them almost as far as Cape Kennedy, at which point he would turn the aircraft virtually round on itself and head out to sea on a bearing of 137 degrees magnetic. That way he would be sure of not only entering Hilda with the wind behind him, but of avoiding her especially dangerous right front quadrant. Once inside her, he would rely entirely on his weather radar to find the eye. It would either be over Hippocrates Cay as the computer had forecast, or it wouldn't, in which case he would have to decide whether Hilda was on course, but late, or off course. If he decided it was the former, he would orbit within the eye until the island came into view; if the latter, he would have no option but to abort the mission and return to base.

The decision as to which type of aircraft to use had been

determined by three overriding considerations: it had to be robust enough to be flown through a hurricane; it had to be capable of landing and taking off fully loaded on a makeshift grass strip in a little under 1,000 feet; and it had to be possible for paratroopers to jump from it.

Cantrel had unhesitatingly plumped for a Buffalo. Like the animal after which it had been named, it had the reputation of surviving the harshest of environments.

But straight away they had run into a problem; although the aircraft had originally been developed specifically at the request of the US Army, an inter-service wrangle back in 1967 had led to a situation where neither the Army nor the USAF any longer had a Buffalo.

The planning officer for Witch-finder had thought of trying to borrow one from either the Brazilian or the Royal Canadian Air Force, but this idea had not been pursued for both logistical and security reasons.

And then someone had remembered that one of the original Army Buffaloes had passed into service with the US Environmental Science Service Administration, where it had been modified to carry equipment for high-altitude photographic surveys.

At the personal request of the President, the ESSA Buffalo had been lent to the USAF, and, as a result of a massive, around-the-clock effort by Air Force and de Havilland engineers, it had not only been re-converted to its original military capability, but the airframe had been strengthened to withstand the massive loadings it would be subjected to during its flight through Hilda.

However, there had been a price to pay for the increase in weight of the modified airframe – they'd had to cut back on both the amount of fuel and the number of people they would carry. Allowing for the fact that they hoped to be returning with prisoners, a freed hostage and a considerable amount of physical evidence, Cantrel had agreed to fly with a two-man crew, and Ackland had reduced his force to twenty men, two of them medics.

As Cantrel strapped in, he was joined by his co-pilot, a young black USAF lieutenant from Tennessee named Novak. Like

Cantrel, he was wearing fatigues and combat boots, and was carrying a Colt .45 in a webbing holster.

'Everyone on board?'

Novak slipped a headset over his khaki baseball cap and began strapping in. 'All saddled up and *rarin'* to go!'

The two men went quickly through their flight compartment checks, auxiliary power unit and engine pre-start checks. By the time they had finished, the crowd of VIPs who had come to see them off had been moved well back from the aircraft.

Chocks were removed, and as soon as he got the rotate props signal, Cantrel reached up to an overhead console and flicked on the START and IGNITION switches. The port then the starboard engines fired and roared into life, turning the three-bladed propellers into almost invisible red-rimmed discs.

Novak pressed the transceiver button on his control yoke and began speaking into his headset microphone. 'Homestead Tower, Buffalo Sierra Alpha Mike Zero One, pre-flight check on one eight decimal three.'

As soon as Cantrel had completed his pre-taxi checks and had switched on the nosewheel steering, Novak said: 'Homestead Tower, SAM Zero One requesting taxi clearance.'

'SAM *Zero One is cleared to holding point*' replied the voice from the tower.

Cantrel released the parking brake. 'Then let's head 'em up and move 'em out!' he yelled, easing back the throttles.

Slowly, the Buffalo rumbled off along the taxiway. Before settling down to check brakes and instruments, Cantrel turned for one last wave at the Attorney-General, who was busy having his photograph taken. 'And screw you too!' he mouthed, grinning amiably.

Born and raised in a remote mining community in the Appalachians, Cantrel didn't much like cops, lawyers or politicians, and as far as he was concerned Forrestal combined the least attractive characteristics of all three. Cantrel was quite sure in his own mind that Operation Witch-finder was nothing more than a blatant attempt at self-aggrandizement on the part of the Attorney-General, and had felt personally affronted by Forrestal's attempts to sell it as some kind of Holy Roman Crusade.

At least he, Cantrel, had not tried to kid anyone about his motives for volunteering for the mission: he was doing it strictly for the money – hazardous-duty pay, plus special-services pay, plus mission-over-hostile-territory pay. For not only was he behind with his alimony, he was also being leaned on by the Mafia-controlled gambling syndicate which held 5,000 dollars' worth of his markers.

Novak had not believed him when – during one of the many games of poker they'd played while waiting for Hilda to move into position – Cantrel had told him why he had volunteered.

'You've gotta be crazy in the head, man!' he had said. 'Flyin' through a hurricane 'cause a chick and a couple of gorillas are puttin' the squeeze on you? Jesus, that's as dumb as having your leg off 'cause you've got an ingrown toenail!'

But as Cantrel had explained, ever since the afternoon of July 27th, 1943, when an instructor at the Instrument Flying School at Bryan, Texas, had taken off in a single engine aircraft to become the first man ever to fly through a hurricane, such flights had become routine.

Novak had not been impressed. 'Shit, man!' he had said. 'How can flyin' through a fuckin' hurricane ever get to be *routine*? Maybe for you it's just another way of gamblin'. Kinda like dealing stud with your life in the pot.' Another more worrying thought had struck him, and he had put down his cards. 'Say, maybe you've got some kind of death wish? Jesus, that's all ah need on a gig like this: a captain with a death wish!'

'The only thing I wish is that you'd play poker,' Cantrel had replied grumpily. 'Anyway, smart-ass, why did you volunteer?'

Novak's black face had split open in a dazzling grin. 'Me? I'm on a big machismo kick, man! Like the rest of the dumb bastards.'

They were now at the runway approach and had completed their pre-flight checklist.

The voice from the Tower said: '*SAM Zero One, clear to line up.*' Cantrel turned on to the runway, applied the wheel brakes, and advanced the power levers. It had almost stopped raining, and ahead of them the sky had begun to lighten faintly along the horizon.

Novak cleared his throat. 'SAM Zero One ready for take-off.'

'SAM Zero One, clear for take-off. And listen, you guys, take it easy, huh?'

Cantrel laughed. 'Wilco!' he said with feeling. He released the wheel brakes, and the runway lights began racing towards them like tracer bullets.

The flight up the eastern coast of Florida was uneventful, and after they had been in the air for just under half an hour Cantrel picked up the PA microphone to talk to his passengers.

'In a couple of minutes we'll be turning on to our approach course,' he announced. 'So if any of you guys back there aren't strapped in, now's the time to do something about it. We expect to be hitting the outer limits of Hilda in about fifteen minutes, and from then on it's going to be like a demolition derby!'

For the past twenty minutes Novak had been flying the Buffalo, while Cantrel handled the navigation and radio communications. But now, after confirming their position with air-traffic control and switching on the de-icing equipment, Cantrel took over the controls.

Novak drew a small circle on the map Cantrel had handed him, and wrote the time beside it. Then, as they began a seventy-degree climbing turn to starboard, he took a last look at the Florida coastline before it disappeared beneath the overcast.

After a couple of minutes spent climbing through a milky whiteness, they broke into bright sunlight.

Waiting for them on the horizon, like a vast outcrop of basalt, was Hilda.

Novak's eyes popped. 'Jesus H. Christ!' he cried. 'That's straight out of *The Devil's Triangle*!'

During the trip up the coast they had both been kept busy, but now that they had the airspace entirely to themselves they could afford to relax for the next ten minutes or so.

'Whadd'ya make of it?' asked Cantrel, as they levelled out.

'*The Devil's Triangle?*' Novak broke open a packet of bubble-gum. 'An dunno if ah go along with all that time-warp, Atlantis jive, but there ain't *no* gettin' away from it – some *pretty* weird things have happened in this neck of the woods . . .'

Cantrel engaged autopilot, took out a cigar and bit off the end. 'Like what?' he asked, lighting it with a big silver Zippo decorated with a pair of black dice.

'Fitzpatrick, for openers. What happened to Fitzpatrick?'

Cantrel shrugged. 'You heard what they said at the briefing.'

'That he probably got zapped ashore?' Novak blew a bubble of gum until it popped. 'Lis'n man, that poor sonuvabitch never got within *sight* of the shore! Goddammit, his dinghy was still on board! So was his piece! Even if he'd swum, leavin' behind his piece was a pretty dumb thing to have done!'

'Anyone dumb enough to think they could take on Snaith single-handed is dumb enough to have forgotten their piece.'

'Okay, well what about the five Navy planes which disappeared between Florida and the Bahamas back in '45?'

'Flight Nineteen, you mean?' Cantrel blew a plume of smoke at the ceiling. 'The guy leading the flight lost his bearings and ran outta fuel.'

'Lost his bearings?' said Novak incredulously. 'C'mon, that cat was a navigation instructor on a training run!'

'Y'know the trouble with you romantics? You won't look at the facts in case it spoils the story.

'Listen, if you lose your cool, the Florida Keys can look a helluva lot like the Bahamas. And we know the guy *did* lose his cool, because he forgot to switch on his clear emergency channel.'

The early morning sun had begun to make the cockpit uncomfortably warm, and Novak reached up and opened the air vent slightly. 'And the Martin Mariner that disappeared durin' the search for Flight Nineteen – what happened to that?'

Cantrel shrugged. 'Martin Mariners had a habit of developing loose fuel connections in turbulence, and there was a thirty-knot wind blowing that day. The *reasonable* explanation is that she simply blew up in mid-air.'

'Okay, so what about the DC-3 that disappeared after the captain reported seeing the lights of Miami? And the *Star Tiger*, the *Star Ariel* and the Superfort that vanished just off of Bermuda?'

'Probably ran into thunderstorms and disintegrated . . .'

'Holy *shit*!' said Novak, glancing nervously at what lay ahead of them. 'If you think they disintegrated in *thunderstorms*, what're we doin' flying into *that* motherfucker?'

Cantrel chuckled. 'The trick is not to let her scare you, and not to fight her. Try to fight her and you're *dead*. After that it's mostly a matter of keeping the wind behind you for as much of the time as possible, and following the SOP for flying through thunderstorms.'

'That'n prayin' a lot!'

Cantrel switched the weather radar to the long-range setting, and a great spiral of phosphorescence appeared on the screen. 'Take a look at this,' he said. 'You can see she's rotating anti-clockwise, okay? And we know she's moving more or less at right angles to our flight path. So, by going into her like this—' using the tip of his cigar, Cantrel traced a line which ran straight up from the bottom of the scope, then turned left to hit the eye from the side '—we'll be flying most of the way with the wind a little to port but as near as dammit up our tail. Also we'll be missing a lot of the crap that's to the east of the eye.'

'But what about comin' out?' Novak asked. 'Assuming we'll be comin' out in a plane and not rosewood caskets . . .'

'Like I said at the briefing, coming out'll be tougher than going in, certainly for the first leg of the journey. What we'll be doing is this . . .' Starting with the tip of his cigar on the eye, he described a line which went a little to the right, turned sharply and then shot straight up to the top of the scope. 'The wind'll be hitting us hard to starboard at first, but once we begin our turn we'll put it pretty much behind us again.'

During the time they had been talking, Hilda appeared to have grown until now she stretched almost the full width of the horizon.

Well before they hit the first of the scud clouds that were circling her slowly turning outer fringe, Cantrel switched from auto to manual control. To minimize the stresses that would be caused by turbulence, he throttled back and re-trimmed. Finally, as a precaution against the temporary blindness that can sometimes be caused by lightning flashes, he turned up the cockpit illumination to its maximum and both men put on sun-glasses.

Wisps of cloud began to fly past the windshield. Then, as

they penetrated the outermost band of cloud, they began to bump about.

'Hey, man,' said Novak, as they broke through into a patch of pale sunlight. 'This ain't *so* bad . . .'

It was not long, however, before they were again swallowed up in cloud. This time the turbulence was more pronounced. The further in they went the darker it became, until eventually all they could see were their own reflections in the windshield.

Although the Buffalo was fitted with discharge wicks, static now began interfering so badly with reception on high and medium frequencies that they had no option but to switch off all their radio equipment. And by the time they had removed their headsets, brush discharge – the ghostly blue light sometimes known as St Elmo's fire – had begun to flicker across the cockpit instrument panels.

They began to pitch and roll alarmingly.

'Guess I spoke too soon,' said Novak, putting out a hand to brace himself against the crash pad.

Then it started to rain. This time, however, the rain came in great swirling masses which drummed so heavily on the Buffalo's duralumin skin that neither man could make himself heard except by shouting.

As soon as the weather radar showed them to be thirty-five nautical miles from the eye, Cantrel began a twenty-degree turn to port. Almost immediately, there was an ear-splitting crack and the atmosphere around them seemed to ignite.

They had been struck by lightning.

There was a smell of ozone and burning rubber, and for several seconds neither man could see anything except the after-image of the flash – a jagged white scar which ran diagonally across the bruised face of the cloud to the tip of their starboard wing.

And then – still in the middle of the turn – they suddenly felt themselves falling. Not the curving fall of a car plunging over a cliff – they seemed to have lost forward momentum altogether. The engine noise rose to a scream and the instruments went berserk.

They must have dropped 200 or 300 feet when their fall was arrested with a thump which made the airframe tremble like a tuning fork. The lights flickered, went out and came on again, and dust began to float from every chink and crevice in the cockpit, sending Cantrel into a paroxysm of coughing.

Out of the corner of his eye, Novak saw something shoot out of Cantrel's pocket and bounce against the cockpit roof.

Instinctively he turned his face away, expecting whatever it was to fall on him. But it didn't. He looked up and saw that it was one of Cantrel's cigars, apparently sticking to the roof.

Turning to the attitude direction indicator, he saw to his horror that instead of the blue half of the disc representing the sky being above the brown, the brown was above the blue.

They were flying upside down.

Hoping to God that he would be able to right the Buffalo before it was hit by another beam gust, Novak took hold of his control yoke and began easing it to starboard.

The cigar rolled slowly across the roof and down the wall, finally coming to rest at Cantrel's feet.

They were the right way up once more.

Still unable to speak for coughing, Cantrel picked up the cigar and handed it to Novak. It was a gesture which conveyed more than any words could ever have done.

For twenty more terrible minutes the Buffalo pitched and rolled and bounced its way through the 200-mile-an-hour winds, its wing roots groaning under the immense loads.

And then, when the picture on the weather radar showed them to be only a few minutes' flying time from the core, Cantrel yelled: 'Well, at least *we've* found the eye. Let's just hope to Christ the eye's found Hippocrates Cay!'

According to the magnetic compass, both they and Hilda were wildly off-course – somewhere out in the mid-Atlantic – but ever since the lightning strike neither man had been taking the instruments very seriously.

Novak switched to MAP on the radar console and a moment later a pattern of white blobs appeared on the scope.

'Looks like we got lucky,' he said, comparing the phosphorescent image with the map he was holding. 'Right now we seem to be passing over the string of islands between Little Abaco and Grand Bahama.'

'Certainly looks that way,' said Cantrel, his eyes flicking between the scope and the mapboard. 'Let's try the radio compass again. We might *just* be able to pick up something from Freeport Tower by now . . .'

Novak did as he had suggested, but got nothing except a blast of static and a needle that swung erratically.

'Oh well, what the hell,' said Cantrel, reaching for the hand mike.

He put it to his lips and switched on. 'General Ackland, we expect to be making the first pass over your DZ in about five minutes, so would you please come to readiness. But take it easy,' he warned. 'We're not out of the turbulence yet.'

Ahead of them it began to lighten, then darken, then lighten again. Soon they were bumping through tattered horizontal layers of cloud pierced by shafts of pale sunlight. Finally, with dramatic suddenness, there was no more cloud and no more turbulence.

It was like coming to the end of a nightmare ride on a runaway rollercoaster.

31

Novak had thought that nothing could ever dwarf the impact of his first sight of Hilda, but what now confronted him was even more awe-inspiring.

They had come out into what looked like an enormous mine-shaft – a shaft so deep that even with his face upturned and touching the windshield he could barely see the sky.

Cantrel, however, was much more preoccupied with what lay below. Just clear of the leading edge of the eye was an island, but one which at first sight was so unlike the briefing model of Hippocrates Cay that he couldn't believe it was the same place. It had been stripped bare of trees and shrubs, and there was nothing to suggest that it had ever had a marina. The staff bungalows were gone, so were the solar panels and the pillars which had once lined the foreshore, and the hospital – if it was the hospital – was an empty shell. Even the shape of the island seemed to have been changed by the onslaught of wind and water; much of the topsoil had been washed away to expose the underlying limestone, and the low-lying northern tip which the photo analysts had nicknamed 'The Dog's Head' had disappeared. Near where it had once been lay a capsized freighter, trapped in a heaving log-jam of fallen trees.

As Cantrel reached for one of the aerial reconnaissance photographs of Hippocrates Cay, the cockpit door opened and Ackland appeared. He was wearing a khaki jumpsuit and helmet, and two parachute packs – one on his back and another on his chest.

'Whadd'ya make of this, then?' Cantrel asked, putting the port wing down to give Ackland a better view. 'Is it the Cay or isn't it? I'd sure as hell hate to put you guys off at the wrong stop!'

'I think it must be,' he replied, leaning over Cantrel's shoulder to compare what he could see through the window with the photograph. 'Look – over to the right – isn't that the lab building?'

Novak switched off the cockpit lights and leaned over to look with them. 'It's the Cay. It's definitely the Cay. Look, you can just make out the helipad under all the crap.'

'I guess you're right at that.' Cantrel levelled up, then turned to Ackland. 'By the way, sorry about the bumpy ride,' he said. 'Were there any casualties?'

'A lot of the guys threw up, in spite of the anti-nauseant. Still, all but maybe two'll be jumping. The medics are working on them now.'

There had been a lot of discussion earlier about the best method of puttting the Rangers on to the island. Basically, Ackland had had to decide whether he would go for a LOLEX or a HALO insertion.

It had not taken him long to rule out LOLEX (an acronym for 'low-level parachute-opening extraction'). The formula ½ speed of aircraft (knots) $\times$ exit time (seconds)=dispersion (metres) revealed that even if the Rangers had jumped with their heels almost on one another's shoulders they would not only have been dispersed too widely for quick, effective deployment, but that there was a very real risk of the first and last man in the stick falling in the sea.

And there was another, even more tricky problem to be considered. The *Special Forces Operational Techniques* manual states that: 'Personnel DZ's located at comparatively high elevations (1,840 metres or higher) will, where possible, use soft snow or grasslands. Because of the increased rate of parachute descent at these altitudes such drops are less desirable than those at or near sea level.'

Although the highest point on Hippocrates Cay was no more than forty feet above sea level, experts from the National Hurricane Research Laboratory had forecast that the barometric pressure within the eye would be half what it would normally have been at sea-level.

This meant that the Rangers would be landing at the kind of speeds to be expected on top of a 9,000-foot-high mountain.

Anyone landing on a hard surface would be very lucky to escape without breaking a leg, or worse.

So, to give them the best possible chance of manoeuvring on to soft ground and in a group, the HALO, or high-altitude low-opening, method had been chosen. Equipped with high-performance steerable parachutes, altimeters specially adapted to compensate for the unusually low pressure, and pneumatic boots, they would jump at 10,000 feet and freefall to 2,000 feet before pulling their rip-cords.

This approach had another advantage: from the time they left the Buffalo to the time they deployed their canopies, they would be invisible to anyone on the ground. After they had opened their canopies, it would only be a little over two minutes before they were on the ground and able to defend themselves.

After Novak had confirmed that the drop course, altitude and speed would be as planned, Ackland returned to the main cabin.

Although the air was rank with the smell of vomit and the distinctively pungent sweat that men exude when they have been badly frightened, most of the Rangers were on their feet, checking to see that none of the buckles and hooks on their harnesses had worked loose.

Ackland made his way through to where the medics were attending to the two Rangers who had been violently airsick. One was lying on the floor, an oxygen mask over his face. The other – a major with a head shaved clean as a billiard ball – was sitting nearby.

'How're you feeling?' Ackland asked.

'Okay, I guess,' the major replied, trying to sound better than he felt.

'Are you up to jumping?'

The major nodded.

The jump ramp began to open, letting in a blast of cold air. 'Are you sure?' yelled Ackland, above the roar of the engines.

Dazzled by the sudden light, the major turned his face away. 'Sure, I'm sure!' he yelled back.

Ackland looked enquiringly at the medics, but all he got were non-committal shrugs.

The Buffalo's engines were throttled back, and then Novak's voice came over the PA to announce that they would be at their release point in three minutes.

The ramp was now fully open and Ackland, followed by the major and a Ranger wearing a helmet-mounted movie camera, crossed to take up their stations alongside the jumpmaster.

'*Two minutes to release point,*' blared the voice from the loudspeakers.

Ackland eased the harness webbing between his legs and pulled his goggles down from off his helmet.

'*One minute to release point.*'

Through the open ramp, Ackland saw the capsized freighter come into view.

The voice from the loudspeakers began the final phase of the countdown.

'*Nine, eight, seven—*' the jump lights turned from red to green '*—six, five, four—*' Ackland took a deep breath and braced himself '*—three, two, one!*'

'Go!' screamed the jumpmaster.

Ackland dived through the hatch into the howling slipstream, and, with his jumpsuit fluttering wildly, spread his arms and legs to form a cross, at the same time arching his back to stabilize his centre of gravity.

Floating like an enormous bird of prey, he peered down through his goggles looking for signs of life.

The major, meanwhile, had made a far less immaculate exit. As soon as he had got up from his seat his legs had begun to tremble. His skin was cold and clammy, and by the time he had taken up his position behind Ackland he was feeling faint.

As Novak had begun the final countdown, the major had told himself that even though he was second-in-command he ought not to jump. If he screwed up on landing, not only would he be useless, he would be a liability to the others. Much better to hold back, he had told himself; there would still be plenty for him to do even after the aircraft had landed.

The major had been about to tell Ackland that he would be stepping aside, when the order to jump had been given.

As Ackland disappeared from the ramp, the jumpmaster had turned to the major. 'Go!' He had hesitated. 'Go!' the jumpmaster had screamed again, but this time – thinking that he had frozen at the last moment – he had pushed him firmly from behind.

Suddenly the major had found himself tumbling through the air. One moment he could see the rapidly receding underbelly of the Buffalo, the next the sea.

He had begun to thrash about, desperately trying to stabilize himself. But the harder he tried, the faster he turned. Soon, he was spinning at a rate of two-and-a-half revolutions a second. His stomach, already badly strained from vomiting, had heaved again, filling his nasal passages with a bloody froth.

Thirty feet to the left of the major, Ackland noticed that he was being overtaken by what at first he thought was an equipment container which had been dropped too soon.

And then he realized what had happened. 'Your rip-cord!' he yelled. 'Pull your rip-cord!'

It was a futile gesture. Even if the major had been able to hear him, he was now so disorientated that he would not have known where to begin looking for his rip-cord.

Ackland decided there was only one thing he could do – try to catch up with the aerodynamically unclean major and pull his rip-cord for him.

Inclining his body to the right, he brought his heels together and swung back his arms into a swallow-diving position. He began to gather speed rapidly. The closer in he brought his arms, the faster he fell. By the time he reached terminal velocity – 200 miles an hour – his face was distorted almost beyond recognition by the force of the airflow.

As he drew level with the major he reached out and made a grab for him. But the major was cartwheeling so fast that, try as he might, it was impossible for him to secure a hold.

With the island racing up towards him, Ackland knew that soon it would be too late for him to open his own parachute, even if he succeeded in opening the major's.

He made one last desperate lunge, but to no avail; it was like trying to catch the sail of a windmill in a gale.

Ackland levelled off, watching helplessly as the doomed man tumbled down towards the waiting island.

With grim irony, the building he ended up in was the roofless hospital. Falling at the speed of an express train, he crashed through the remains of the first floor, hitting a table in the operating suite below with a force which split him open and shattered every bone in his body.

A great flock of bedraggled birds, gathered up within the eye during Hilda's journey along the islands, rose shrieking from within the hospital.

Alarmed to see that the needle of his jump altimeter was already well into the red danger zone, Ackland pulled his rip-cord. The securing pin flew away and the parachute rippled out of his backpack, blossoming above him.

He looked down, aware for the first time just how badly off course he had drifted during his rescue attempt. Instead of being above the centre of the island he was over the freighter and drifting out to sea.

Taking a firm grip on his control lines, he turned his canopy so that the air that was being deflected through the vent would propel him inland.

He was now heading in the right direction, but falling fast. And lying in his direct line of drift was the great yawning shell of the hospital.

It was then that he noticed the birds. The air ahead of him was full of the creatures: herons, gulls, spoonbills, crows and many more he did not recognize.

A moment later he was among them. They flew past him, collided with him, tried to settle on him. Soon, scores were flut-tering panic-stricken within his canopy.

In the distance he heard the blasting caps on the equipment containers begin to fire, forcing his attention back to the question of where to land.

He would have liked to dog-leg around the ruin and drive up to where the other Rangers would be landing in a few moments. But he had just noticed that two of the island's guards were racing to intercept him, one armed with an axe.

If he was going to avoid either crashing in the middle of the ruin or being chopped at as he floated over the men's heads there was only one thing he could do: he would have to knock off as much drift as possible, as quickly as possible.

He reached up, grabbed his two front lift webs and pulled them sharply down, spilling air from under the canopy. Straight away he lost all forward momentum and most of the lift. The ground rushed up towards him, and he barely had time to tuck in his chin and flex his knees before he had thudded into the rain-sodden earth.

As he rolled over he snapped open his quick-release harness box, and was on his feet even before his canopy had begun to collapse.

It was not a moment too soon.

The first of the guards to reach him, a massively built negro with a fist full of rings, hurled himself forward. Ackland side-stepped, and, as the negro stumbled past him, swung around and struck him a shattering blow on the back of his exposed neck.

As the negro splashed down into the mud, the second guard – a giant of a man with a bushy red beard – swung his axe. Ackland dropped to his knees, and, as the blade whistled over his head, sprang forward and butted him hard in the stomach. With a gasp of pain, the guard collapsed on top of him. Ackland grabbed hold of the guard's ankles and straightened up, sending him somersaulting over his shoulders. As he crashed on to his back, Ackland swivelled around and drove the heel of his steel-tipped jump boot hard down on the bridge of the guard's nose.

Ackland pushed his goggles up on to his helmet and wiped the sweat from his eyes. So much intense activity in the stiflingly hot, rarefied air had set his heart thumping like a trip-hammer. While he waited to get his breath back he turned and took stock of the situation.

He was, he saw, standing in what had been a flower-bed at the north end of the lawn on which the circling Buffalo would soon be landing. Through the trembling heat-haze he could see that the turf was covered by a thin sheet of water. Sticking out of the water was debris of every kind – bricks and splintered planks of wood, broken boughs, uprooted shrubs, furniture and hospital equipment. There was even an upturned motor boat which had apparently been rolled up from the shore like tumbleweed.

The birds which had risen when the major had crashed into the hospital had settled. Some stood preening their bedraggled feathers, but most just sat listlessly, watching him with exhausted eyes.

By now, most of the Rangers had landed and Ackland picked up his 12-gauge Remington slide-repeater shotgun and moved off to join them.

As the birds directly in his path spread their wings and took to the air, a thought occurred to him that stopped him dead in his tracks.

The Buffalo – as well as landing and taking off on a strip like a wet sponge – was going to have to fly in and out again through air thick with birds!

Although no one had anticipated that they might be faced with such a problem, it had been agreed that if for any reason the Buffalo could not land, he and his men would take their chances in the laboratory while Hilda's rear wall passed over the island.

Ackland took out his binoculars and scanned the building. To the naked eye it seemed to have survived unscathed, but he could now see that many of the slender concrete pillars on which it was supported had begun to crumble, and that there was a zigzag crack running all the way down the curtain wall.

During his early training as an artillery officer, he had learned enough about structural engineering to know that with the return of the 200-mile-an-hour winds and the storm surges the building would collapse and be swept away.

'Brunelli, over here!' he yelled to his radio-telephone operator.

Taking cover behind the upturned motor boat, he grabbed the microphone from the RTO's backpack and pressed the transmitter button. 'Able leader to Baker leader.'

The radio crackled, and Novak came through, blaringly loud. *'Baker leader, reading you strength four.'*

'Strength five,' replied Ackland, as two Rangers carrying chainsaws raced by to begin clearing the lawn. 'Listen, we've got problems down here. We're up to our asses in birds.'

'Say again?'

'The place is covered with *birds*! B Bravo, I India, R—'

'Birds! Roger you. How many birds?'

'Thousands. I don't know how you're going to get down through 'em, there're so many of the bastards . . .'

'Christ!' he heard Novak say. *'Able leader, is there any way you can assist?'*

'Negative.'

'Aren't you carrying shotgun rounds? Over.'

'Affirmative. But there are too many of them – we'd be here till Christmas.'

'*What about tear-gas?*'

'In the open, without a breath of wind? Hopeless.'

'*How do you feel about staying?*' asked Novak.

'I'm not crazy about the idea.'

'*You got a problem there, too, Able leader?*'

Ackland hesitated, knowing that once he told them about the condition of the laboratory they would come in and get him whatever the risks to themselves.

'*So c'mon, tell Momma all about it!*' insisted Novak.

'Well, it looks to me like the lab's all ready to collapse . . .'

'*Stand by.*'

Ackland knew he had gone off the air to confer with Cantrel, and while he waited he swept aside the birds sitting on the keel of the boat and took a look over the top.

The Rangers had fanned out and were moving forward, flitting from cover to cover, while the captain who had taken over as second-in-command was using a loudhailer to call on the men inside the laboratory to come out with their hands above their heads.

'*Able leader, Baker leader,*' the radio suddenly blared. '*We're coming in as soon as you give us the words, right? We'll fly in as slow as we dare and hope we don't get too many strikes. Acknowledge.*'

Ackland let out his breath. 'Acknowledge!'

'*Hey, what's the LZ like, man?*'

'It's under about half-an-inch of water . . .'

'*Terrific!*' said Novak. '*That's all I need – birds and a saturated LZ!*'

Ackland replaced the microphone on the RTO's backpack. 'Okay,' he said, 'let's go.'

With their heads held low, the two men broke cover and began running towards the other Rangers.

They were almost half-way across the stretch of open ground when Ackland saw a flash in one of the embrasures near the door of the laboratory building.

Yelling a warning to his RTO, he threw himself face down. Something plopped into the water a few yards ahead of him, and, as the other Rangers opened fire, there was a brilliant orange flash and the ground rose into the air with a deafening roar.

With mud still raining down on his back, Ackland turned to see what had become of the RTO. He was on his hands and knees staring blankly at him.

'Are you all right, soldier?' he yelled. The words were hardly out of his mouth when a great loop of purple gut slithered through a hole in the RTO's jumpsuit.

Grabbing hold of his first-aid pack, Ackland began to make his way towards the wounded man. But he had not got far when a line of machine-gun bullets zipped past him and cut the man down. Soon, the water through which he was crawling began to turn red, and by the time he got to him, the RTO was dead.

The incoming fire had now almost ceased, and Ackland – clutching the big battlefield radio to his chest – raced across the remaining stretch of open ground and threw himself down alongside Captain Meninsky, his second-in-command.

Although none of the other Rangers seemed to have been hit during the exchange of fire, it was impossible to know what casualties, if any, had been caused among the men behind the embrasures.

Once again, Meninsky picked up his loudhailer and called on them to come out, but still there was no response.

'Looks kinda like we're goin' to have to go in and get 'em,' he said, turning to Ackland.

During the planning of Witch-finder, Army Intelligence officers had interrogated representatives of the security company which had installed the electrically operated sliding steel door to the building. 'Don't waste time trying to blow a hole in the door,' they had been told. 'Go for the concrete around it.'

Tests had shown this to be sound advice, and explosive experts had equipped the assault squad with portable radio-detonated magnetic mines designed to demolish the concrete door-case.

However, now that he was less than thirty feet from the building, Ackland could see that the ground beneath it had subsided, and that the crack running from the roof down past the left-hand side of the door was even worse than it had looked through his binoculars. At its widest point it was big enough for him to have put his fist in. If he did use the magnetic mines, he risked bringing the building down along with the door.

And yet Snaith clearly wasn't coming out, and with the windows covered with steel shutters, there was no other way in. All Ackland could do, therefore, was to blow the door. If the building collapsed, that was just too bad.

'Okay, Captain,' he said, jacking a shell into the chamber of his shotgun. 'Let's go.'

Meninsky repeated the order into his walkie-talkie, and two Rangers who had taken up positions near the steps began pulling on breathing apparatus.

As soon as they signalled that they were ready, Meninsky put the walkie-talkie to his lips again. 'Standby, smoke team,' he said. 'Three, two, one. *Go!*'

Half-a-dozen grenades fell in front of the building and exploded in unison, enveloping it in billowing clouds of thick green smoke.

The Rangers wearing breathing apparatus ran into the smoke and up the steps to the door, where, operating by touch alone, they began placing the mines.

Ackland heard the magnetic hold-fasts snap one after another against the door, and the sound of the Rangers' feet pounding back down the steps. As soon as they were clear of the smoke and behind cover, he gave the order to fire.

Meninsky turned the key on his radio detonator. There was a tremendous explosion which lit up the smoke for an instant, then sent it rolling out over the bowed heads of the Rangers.

Ackland looked up. Although one half of the building was now unmistakably out of alignment with the other, it was still standing. So, too, was the door.

And then he saw it begin to fall slowly forwards. It picked up speed. The steel handrail at the top of the steps crumpled beneath its enormous weight, and, with a resounding clang, it came to rest amid a cloud of dust on the concrete landing.

32

'Go!' yelled Meninsky. 'Go, go, go!'

Followed by the rest of the Rangers, Ackland sprang to his feet, stormed up the steps and through the doorway.

Ahead of him he could see men scrambling up the stairs leading to the first floor. 'Hold it!' he yelled, putting his shotgun to his shoulder. 'Hold it or I'll fire!'

He waited a moment, and then squeezed the trigger. A pattern of ragged holes appeared across the back of the nearest of the running men, and, with the thunder of the shot still reverberating around the hall, he stumbled and fell. Almost immediately, Meninsky fired at the fallen man – he had seen him pull the pin from a hand-grenade. 'Down!' he yelled.

As the Rangers hurled themselves to the floor, the grenade exploded, blowing the man apart.

Lights flickered, went out and came on again, and a couple of tiles dropped from the suspended ceiling.

And then something failed deep within the fabric of the building. A picture fell from the wall, and, with a gathering roar, the building began to tremble.

Suddenly the whole of the ceiling crashed down upon the backs of the Rangers, exposing a tangle of air-conditioning ducts and conduits. A great billowing cloud of dust rose into the air, and Ackland – expecting at any moment to be entombed – felt the floor sag beneath him.

It was like being in an earthquake. Through the deep, grinding roar he could hear the tinkle of breaking glass and the sharp, explosive crackle of splintering wood.

Gradually the tumult died down, to be replaced by an awesome silence broken only by coughing and the distant sound of water gushing from fractured pipes.

Ackland lifted his head. Through the swirling dust he could see that the floor had split from the front of the building to the back, and that one half was now a foot lower than the other.

Dazed and covered with dust, he scrambled to his feet, and, followed by Meninsky and six other Rangers, picked his way through the debris and began cautiously climbing the blood-splattered stairs.

Once on the landing, Ackland and his sub-unit turned to the right, Meninsky and his men to the left.

Ahead of him, Ackland could see a fireproof door. With his finger on the trigger, he sidled up to it and looked warily through the observation window. He could see a long, gloomy passageway and more doors, several of them hanging off their hinges. The floor was covered with debris, and sitting on an overturned trolley was a small, shivering monkey which had escaped from a nearby animal room.

Curiously, for he was not a man given to morbid imaginings, the passageway seemed steeped in an atmosphere of such palpable, overwhelming melancholy that for a moment he was reluctant to enter.

'Trouble?' someone asked, in a hoarse whisper.

Ackland shook his head. 'Let's go,' he said, shouldering open the swing-door.

After leaping on to an emergency eye-wash basin, the monkey turned to watch as the Rangers silently took up positions on either side of the first door – Ackland and a corporal carrying a sledge-hammer to the left, a sergeant named Flynn to the right.

Gently, Ackland tried the handle, but the door wouldn't budge. Flattening himself against the wall, he took a tight grip on his shotgun and nodded.

The corporal spat on his hands, and, standing well clear of the door, swung the hammer hard against the lock. With a crash that sent the monkey scampering off down the passageway, the door flew open.

Immediately, Ackland and Flynn dived into the room, one to the left, the other to the right.

They were in a big, brightly lit laboratory, smelling of formaldehyde and ether. And they were not alone.

Standing behind a wooden bench in the middle of the room – her eyes wide with terror – was a pretty, fair-haired girl in a blue dressing-gown. It was Clair Tennant. Behind her was Lee Quintrell. One of his hands was clamped over her mouth, while the other held an automatic to the side of her head. Crouched on either side of him were Ginzel and Sanchez. Each was holding a Colt Python in a double-handed grip – one pointed at Ackland, the other at Flynn.

'If either of you makes a wrong move, the girl gets it!' shouted Quintrell. He was pale and dishevelled, and one of the lenses was missing from his spectacles. 'Now, drop your guns and get your hands behind your heads.'

Ackland began to chuckle. 'Listen, fella, you know what'll happen if you fire that thing? Your buddies'll get blown away. Then you'll have to decide who it'll be, me or him,' he said, nodding at Flynn. 'Because I'll tell you this: whichever of us *doesn't* get it will get you. Now, do yourself a favour and quit while you're still ahead of the game.'

Dragging Clair along with him, Quintrell began backing toward a door to an adjoining room.

With only forty-five minutes left before they would have to leave, there was, Ackland knew, no question of his sitting it out until Quintrell cracked. He had to do something, and he had to do it now. What would happen, he wondered, if he and Flynn were to gun down Ginzel and Sanchez? Would they have time to squeeze off a round before the shot got to them? And would Quintrell kill the girl, despite the fact that she was only of use to him while she was alive?

But by now the three men were not only closer to the door, they were closer to one another; so close that Ackland knew if either he or Flynn fired they were bound to wound the girl.

With his revolver still aimed at Ackland's chest, Ginzel turned the door handle and Quintrell began backing into the darkened room.

He had not got far when someone struck him a savage blow behind the knees. Taking Clair with him, he fell backwards on to the floor.

And then, before either of the men covering Quintrell's exit had had a chance to react, Ackland fired.

A cluster of shot scythed through a rack of test-tubes on top of the first of the benches, hit Ginzel full in the chest and sent him crashing into a shelf full of laboratory glass.

Sanchez swung around, fired at Ackland and began running

for cover. With the big .38 bullet still wanging its way around the room, Flynn fired at Sanchez. A glass tank full of white mice exploded in a shower of rainbow-coloured fragments. Sanchez shrieked and blood spattered the wall behind him, but still he kept running.

Flynn chambered another round and fired again. This time the whole of the tightly bunched cluster found its target. Sanchez clutched at his face, and, with blood spurting from between his fingers, ran head first into a cabinet full of brightly coloured molecular models and collapsed.

Ackland and Flynn darted forward to see what was happening in the adjoining room.

Quintrell was lying with the back of his head in a rapidly widening pool of blood and his heels drumming the floor. Standing over him – with one foot on Quintrell's automatic – was Michael Fitzpatrick. He was wearing only a pair of pyjama trousers and slippers, and his right shoulder was heavily bandaged. Clair was sitting on the floor with her face pressed to his thigh, sobbing.

Throwing aside the intravenous stand he had been holding, Fitzpatrick helped Clair to her feet. 'Boy, oh boy!' he said, taking her into his arms. 'Am I glad to see you guys . . .'

The Rangers exchanged puzzled glances. 'Hey, man,' said Flynn, 'we thought you were dead!'

Fitzpatrick began explaining what had happened, but Ackland stopped him. 'Sorry, but with this place about to crumble like a stale cookie, it's going to have to wait,' he said, peering past him into the gloom of the adjoining room. 'What's in there?'

'God knows,' replied Fitzpatrick, turning to look over his shoulder. 'We've been kept locked in a room at the end of the corridor.'

'How come you got in there, then?' asked Ackland, stepping aside to allow Flynn to drag Quintrell out by his heels.

'When the building subsided after the last explosion, the door split open. I came looking for Clair, saw what was happening, and—' Fitzpatrick nodded at a huge rent in the passageway wall '—well, I guess I just sort of squeezed in . . .'

Leaders of sub-units began coming through on Ackland's walkie-talkie to report that they had secured the various parts of the building assigned to them.

'Any sign of Snaith?' he asked, indicating to Flynn that he was to take Fitzpatrick and Clair downstairs.

'*We have him in the entrance hall*,' somebody replied.

After ordering his unit leaders to release as many men as possible to help with the clearing of the airstrip, Ackland pocketed his walkie-talkie and went into the adjoining room. A wind began to moan in the fissure through which Fitzpatrick had entered, and once again he became aware of the same air of irredeemable melancholy he had first noticed in the passageway.

As his eyes became accustomed to the gloom, he began to see that the room was full of large, cylindrical glove-boxes. Each was surrounded by stands holding intravenous bottles and an array of mysterious-looking machines which clicked, and buzzed, and gave off strange, sonar-like bleeps.

He switched on his flashlight. The floor was covered with fallen ceiling tiles, papers and X-ray films. Foraging amongst the litter were scores of large, white laboratory rats with eyes that glowed like tiny pin-points of fire.

Ackland swung his flashlight on to the nearest of the glove-boxes, and felt himself grow suddenly cold. Inside, apparently floating on a cushion of air, was a young, olive-skinned woman. She was festooned with electrode wires, intravenous lines and drainage tubes, and the whole of her abdominal sheath, her breasts and much of her ribcage had been cut away to reveal her internal organs.

Taking a step nearer, he saw that between the woman's undulating lungs lay a vigorously beating heart.

After calling for a medic and a photographer, he moved on to the next cot. It, too, contained a patient – a man – who'd had his insides exposed in the same manner.

At the sound of approaching footsteps, Ackland looked over his shoulder and saw that Fitzpatrick had returned.

'Come and take a look at this.'

Fitzpatrick crossed and peered into the cot. 'Holy Mother of God!' he cried, his face puckering with disgust.

'Just what the hell's been going on here?'

'Snaith didn't tell me a damned thing.'

'Nothing?'

Fitzpatrick shook his head. 'I guess it's only in thrillers that the villain ever does . . .' He bent to examine the man's glistening insides more closely. 'You know, I think this guy's had a heart-lung transplant – I'm sure they're sutures I can see around his trachea and aorta . . .' Slipping his hand into the latex glove nearest the man's head, he carefully lifted an eyelid. The pupil was fully dilated.

Ackland shone his flashlight around the crowded room. 'Just what the fuck am I supposed to *do* with them all?' he asked indignantly. 'There's no way we're going to be able to get the poor bastards on the plane with us . . . .'

Fitzpatrick turned to look at the oscilloscope standing beside the man's cot. 'It wouldn't even be worth trying,' he replied, after watching the fluorescent blip traverse the screen for a moment. 'According to his EEG he's already dead.'

'Dead?' Ackland swung his flashlight back on to the pounding heart. 'How can he be dead if—'

He stopped, his attention taken by Flynn, who had reappeared in the doorway. 'General, there's something I'd like you to come and look at,' he said, sounding badly shaken.

Ackland and Fitzpatrick followed him through the laboratory and down a long, draughty passageway awash with a foaming blue liquid that smelled of disinfectant. They turned a corner and found two more Rangers waiting for them outside a room loud with the clamour of alarm bells.

Fitzpatrick walked up to the door and looked inside. Through the swirling dust he could see row upon row of what appeared to be combined heart-lung and kidney machines, all of them covered with rubble and smashed infra-red light fittings. Although he knew his eyes must be deceiving him, each of the machines was surmounted by what looked like a skinned monkey in a goldfish bowl. Seabirds – which had got into the room through an enormous hole in the outside wall – were squabbling over the remains of one of the monkeys whose bowl had been smashed.

Fitzpatrick picked his way across to the nearest of the

machines and wiped the dust from the glass sphere with a sterile gown.

What, from the doorway, had looked like a monkey turned out to be a living male foetus. Its eyes were closed, and it was floating weightlessly in a straw-coloured liquid, anchored to the bottom of the vessel by a coiled umbilical cord. A network of veins could be seen through its translucent skin, and it was covered with pale-gold lanugo.

Throwing aside the gown, he began examining the machine. By now, the wind had set doors banging throughout the building. After a moment he turned to the men in the doorway. 'I think this is some sort of a – some sort of artificial womb.' He began pointing out various components. 'Look, there's an oxygenator and an extractor, an auto-analyser, a heat exchanger, blood filter and bubble trap.' He picked up a clipboard that was hanging from a hook on the front of the machine and began leafing through the fluttering sheets. 'I thought so; there's a lot of stuff here about nutrients, pH levels and Christ knows what else . . .'

'I remember reading somewhere about an Italian guy who said he'd grown test-tube babies in an artificial womb,' said Flynn.

Fitzpatrick nodded. 'Petrucci. His name was Daniele Petrucci. But he was an embryologist. I can understand why an embryologist would've been interested in artificial wombs, but not a *heart* surgeon. It doesn't make sense . . . .

'Except, wait a minute!' he added, 'it's just occurred to me – I think, in fact I'm pretty damned sure I know what this is all about!'

Ackland interrupted him to point at what looked like the door to a bank vault he had just noticed at the far end of the room. 'See if you can get it open,' he told Flynn, before turning back to Fitzpatrick. 'I'm listening . . .'

'Four or five years ago, Snaith got himself into hot water with a scheme for cloning genetic replicas. The idea was that he'd use the replicas as a source of non-rejectable organs. So, my hunch is that we'll find that the people in the other room have had all their major organs replaced with ones taken from foetuses grown from their own body cells.'

226

'All their organs?' Ackland frowned. 'Who ever needs to have *all* his organs transplanted? And anyway, why's he cut away half of the poor bastards' ribs and gut?'

'They must be human guinea pigs. They can't be anything else. Human guinea pigs Snaith's had opened up so he can keep tabs on what happens to the organs after they've been transplanted.

'If you want quick, unequivocal results,' Fitzpatrick added, 'I guess this is the way to get 'em.'

'But Snaith's a *doctor*,' Ackland protested. 'How can a doctor—'

'—do what Snaith's done?' Fitzpatrick shrugged. 'It was doctors who conducted all those experiments on the inmates of concentration camps during the last war . . .'

'Okay, but where's Snaith been getting his guinea pigs?' asked Ackland, turning in time to see Flynn take hold of the door handle and swing it open. 'For Christ's sake, this isn't Nazi Germany.'

'India,' suggested Fitzpatrick, as they began picking their way across to Flynn. 'I don't expect too many questions are asked about the occasional missing person in Bombay.'

By the time they arrived alongside him, he had begun exploring the dark, bitterly cold chamber with his flashlight. In front of them they could see a row of chairs and a control console; beyond it a stainless-steel bench.

Flynn moved the beam along the top of the bench until he encountered a hollow box made from what looked like scaled-down steel scaffolding. Something was hanging within the construction, but the flare coming off the network of highly polished rods made it impossible to see what it was.

And then something began to move just in front of them – something which made a sound like scratching fingernails.

Flynn swung the beam back on to the console and they saw that a set of chart pens had begun drawing a pattern of spiky lines on the roll of slowly turning graph paper which lay beneath them.

'What the hell set that going?' asked Fitzpatrick.

Immediately, another set of pens began moving.

'I'll be damned!' he said. 'Whatever it was, it obviously responded to the light and then to the sound of my voice!'

Flynn raised the beam and hit yet another of the curious hollow boxes, but this time at an angle which did not cause a flare. Now they could see only too clearly what was suspended within it.

It was a severed human head, its mouth held shut by a jaw bandage. Hanging from the carefully dissected-out and sutured neck was a cat's cradle of varicoloured tubes and wires.

As one of the sets of pens began scratching more frantically than the others, they noticed that the eyeballs beneath the sewn-up lids had begun flicking rapidly from side to side.

Ackland's walkie-talkie suddenly began to crackle, making the watching men start. *'General, it's Meninsky. Is there any chance of you getting across to the west wing. We've got something kinda spooky over here . . .'*

'You've got something spooky over *there*?' replied Ackland, forcing himself to speak calmly. 'Christ, man, you should be where *we* are!'

Meninsky came back sounding puzzled. *'Say again?'*

'Forget it! We'll be right over.'

'Brain transplants?' said Ackland, as they hurried towards the west wing. 'I thought brain transplants were just science fiction . . .'

'Brain transplants, maybe,' replied Fitzpatrick. 'But not whole-head transplants. Neurosurgeons in Cleveland have been transplanting monkey heads since the early '70s. Sure, they've always rejected, but until they did they functioned perfectly normally. And rejection wouldn't be a problem if you were transplanting on to cloned bodies; then, the only problem would be getting the two spinal cords to grow together – something the Russians claim is now possible.'

'You're not suggesting that the heads back there are still alive, are you? How can they be, for chrissake? Decapitation's one of the few really sure ways of killing someone instantly.'

'Decapitation only kills because the brain is deprived of blood,' Fitzpatrick explained. 'Keep the head supplied with oxygenated blood and nutrients, and there's no reason why it shouldn't function more or less indefinitely.

'According to the EEG trace, the ones we saw were producing beta rhythms,' he added, as they turned the corner on to the landing, 'and the brain only produces beta rhythms when it's awake and thinking . . .'

A member of Meninsky's squad led them down a length of flooded passageway and into an aquarium lit by a single shaft of sunlight that was streaming through a crack in the ceiling. Standing in front of a tank half-way down the room was Meninsky. 'Oh, boy,' he said, as they began splashing their way across to him, 'you're *never* goin' to believe what's in here!'

Using their cupped hands as blinkers, Ackland and Fitzpatrick put their faces to the cold glass.

At first they could see nothing except particles of floating debris. Then, as a curious chirruping began to issue from speakers somewhere above their heads, a creature unlike any they had ever seen before emerged from the gloom at the back of the tank.

The size of a large walrus, its torpedo-shaped body was covered with smooth, almost translucent skin, and it had four gill-slits on either side of its massive head. Its eyes, which were set below brow-ridges like those of a gorilla, were large and strangely comprehending, and it had a protuberant muzzle bristling with long, wiry hairs and flexible lips. Its neck and shoulders were covered with a mane of black hairs about three inches in length. Set just behind the gill-slits were a pair of anterior limbs like a human arm, each ending in a hand with webbed fingers and an opposable thumb.

After surveying the men for a moment, the creature turned, and, propelling itself with its flipper-like hind legs, disappeared into the gloom.

'Well, what do you make of it?' asked Meninsky.

'God knows.' Ackland glanced at his watch. 'We've got a couple of minutes before we have to leave – why don't we get Snaith up here and ask *him*?'

Meninsky took out his walkie-talkie, and, as he passed on the order, Ackland asked Fitzpatrick what he made of it.

'It's got to be some kind of chimera—'

'A *what*?'

'A man-animal hybrid. Listen, either Snaith or someone on

his team must be capable of some pretty formidable nuclear surgery to have cloned genetic replicas. So, producing a man-animal hybrid would be no great trick; genetic engineers have been fusing human cells and animal cells for years now . . . The question's not how he's done it, but why. My guess is that he's been trying to breed something that's as intelligent as man, is able to communicate with man, and has man's manipulative skills. A sort of super-dolphin.

'And when you think about it, it's not *all* that crazy an idea. Two-thirds of the earth's surface is covered with ocean, and we know it's an as yet untapped source of minerals, food and energy. So, something like this could have an enormous commercial as well as a defence application.'

Meninsky – who had gone out into the passageway to await Snaith's arrival – suddenly yelled: 'We're in here!'

A moment later two Rangers dragged a man dressed in a torn oilskin into the room.

'Well, here he is,' said one of the Rangers, grabbing a handful of the man's hair and jerking his head back so that his face could be seen. 'But there's no way you'll get a lick of sense outta the li'l fucker. We ain't even sure he understands English!'

The man had the same long, boney face, acquiline nose and lobeless ears as Snaith, and, like Snaith, his bushy eyebrows joined in the middle. His hair, however, was black, and his pale skin was without a wrinkle.

'That's not *Snaith*!' exclaimed Fitzpatrick.

Ackland exchanged blank looks with the man's escort. 'How do you mean, it isn't *him*?' he demanded, trying to keep feelings of mounting panic out of his voice. Unbuttoning one of the pockets in the leg of his soiled jumpsuit, he took out a plastic bag full of photographs, and, with trembling fingers, passed one to Fitzpatrick. 'Look, of course it's him, goddammit!'

'But this picture must have been taken at least fifteen years ago!'

'It was the only one of him they could find.'

'Okay, but Snaith looks a hell of a lot older now. His hair's turned white—'

'So he's had it dyed . . .'

Fitzpatrick shook his head emphatically. 'Listen, I've seen

Snaith and I'm telling you – this guy isn't him! Snaith's at least thirty years older!'

'Well, it isn't his son,' grumbled Ackland. 'He doesn't have any children. And before you ask, he doesn't have a younger brother either.'

'He must have,' Fitzpatrick insisted, walking up to the man and lifting his top lip with his thumb. 'Look, he's even got the same gap between his—' He suddenly stopped and turned to stare at Ackland. 'It's just struck me – if this guy isn't Snaith's son or his brother, he must be his *clone*! My God, I think he's cloned himself!

'And you know something else – something that might account for him not being able to talk? I don't think anybody's ever bothered to *teach* him to talk! I think he's nothing more than a living spare-parts kit for Snaith!

'In fact I'd go further than that; I think that when Snaith's body finally wears out, he's intending to have his head transplanted on to this poor sod's body!'

33

'Roger, Able leader,' said Cantrel, as soon as the call came requesting him to land. 'We thought you'd never ask!'

Even working with chainsaws and explosives, it had taken the Rangers and their prisoners much longer to clear the lawn than had been expected, and it was still saturated with water.

Novak brought the Buffalo around for the last time and lined up. Ahead of him lay the capsized freighter, beyond it rocks and the start of the 40-foot-wide, 950-foot-long strip of debris-free lawn. On the opposite side of the lawn, like buffers at the end of a railway track, was the concrete laboratory.

Although Novak was worried about the birds which were beginning to rise into the air ahead of him, he was not *too* worried. Provided they didn't smash a hole in the windshield, and providing they weren't sucked into the engine air-intakes, he expected to get down in one piece.

It was what might happen *after* he was down that was making him sweat. Come in a little too fast, or touch down a little too late, or aquaplane, and there was no way he was going to be able to avoid crashing into the laboratory. Although it wouldn't save him or Cantrel, the most they would be able to do during their final seconds would be to shut down the port engine and kick on left rudder in the hope of leaving some part of the building standing for the others to shelter in.

Novak lowered flaps and undercarriage, reduced power still further and eased back on the control column so that the Buffalo went in with her nose up, balanced on the very edge of a stall.

As the freighter disappeared beneath them there was an enormous thump and a splash of blood across the windshield.

They had hit the first of the birds.

A moment later another bird exploded against the windshield, and then another – this time frosting the plexiglass.

Cantrel switched on the wipers, but they did nothing except cover the whole of the windshield with a film of blood.

Soon, the plane was shuddering under the impact of the hail

of birds, and Novak was having to wrestle with the controls to keep it on anything like level flight. An almost unbroken stream of red vapour and feathers began to pour from behind each of the propellers.

The landing was almost blind, Novak relying on Cantrel's commentary as he judged their height through the side window. As Cantrel shouted 'Now!', Novak chopped the throttles and felt for the ground. The starboard wheels jarred into the grass, bounced, then dropped again, throwing up a bow wave like a power boat.

Novak glanced to the right and saw that the tip of the starboard wing was skimming the surface of the water like a pebble.

Both men braced themselves, expecting the wing to be torn from its root at any moment.

Miraculously, it didn't happen. Instead, the Buffalo heeled over in the opposite direction and the port wheels made contact with the grass.

With the building rushing towards them, Cantrel applied full reverse thrust and Novak tried maximum anti-skid braking.

But a moment later he had to release the brakes – he could feel the Buffalo beginning to aquaplane on the sodden grass.

Although the building was getting bigger every second, all he could do was wait for the patch of dry ground ahead of them.

Out of the corner of his eye he saw Cantrel reach out, ready to switch off the port engine if a collision became inevitable.

After the longest couple of seconds of their lives, they finally arrived at the dry ground and Novak hit the brakes.

They began to loose speed fast, and although they were still being bombarded, the birds were no longer disintegrating against the aircraft.

Finally, the blood-stained Buffalo rolled to a standstill, with just enough room for Novak to bring it around 360 degrees on its locked starboard wheel, ready for take off.

Ackland returned once more to the building, which the vibration from the Buffalo's engines had set groaning like a ship in a heavy sea. With him was Fitzpatrick and two Rangers carrying cans of gasolene they had found in the emergency-generator room.

Waiting inside the hall were ten guards, each lashed to a chair. The chairs had been placed in a row facing the open doorway, six feet apart.

'Okay,' said Ackland, massaging the harness bruises on his shoulders. 'So has anybody decided to tell me what I want to know?'

One of the guards began complaining that his civil rights had been violated, but the rest remained silent.

'Write your Congressman,' said Ackland, turning to nod at the Rangers. Immediately, they picked up their jerry-cans and began moving along the line of prisoners, soaking each of them in turn with gasoline. As they emptied one can they flung it aside and uncapped another.

As soon as they had finished, Ackland set fire to a piece of rolled-up paper. 'Now, you've got exactly ten seconds to tell me where I can find Snaith,' he said, returning the lighter to the Ranger from whom he'd borrowed it, 'and then I'm going to start lighting up you sons of bitches.'

Ackland counted from one to ten, and then, shaking his head sadly, strolled across to the red-bearded guard who had tried to kill him earlier.

The guard, who was by now enveloped in a trembling haze of gasolene fumes, turned his blood-caked face away from the flames. 'You crazy bastard!' he cried. 'Where do you *think* he is? He's here in the building . . .'

'I *know* he's in the building,' said Ackland, turning the paper so that it burned more fiercely. 'I want to know *where* in the building.'

'I don't know! I swear to *God* I don't know!'

Ackland backed away. 'Okay, if that's the way you want to play it,' he said, and then, as Cantrel appeared at the door tossed the burning paper down near the guard's feet.

In spite of being bound to a chair, he somehow managed to throw himself clear of the flames. As he crashed to the floor his companions began shouting and cursing.

Fitzpatrick dashed forward and stamped on the burning paper – through the uproar he had heard what they wanted to know. 'This way,' he yelled at Ackland, glancing at his wrist watch. 'If we get our skates on, we can just about make it!'

Ignoring Cantrel's pleas to leave before it was too late, they raced up the stairs three steps at a time, along the right-hand passageway and into the room where they had first met.

Taking Ackland's flashlight from him, Fitzpatrick moved quickly down the line of cots until, in the last one, he found what he was looking for – a naked man with grey hair on his chest and his head enveloped in a bandage.

'That's him – I'm *sure* of it.'

Ackland shrugged. 'If you say so.' Taking hold of the barrel of his shotgun with both hands, he raised it above his head and swung the stock hard down on to the lid of the cot.

The plastic frosted over, and the man inside twitched.

Ackland's second blow smashed a hole in the lid, and the man suddenly curled up into a foetal position.

With the man twisting and turning in a frantic attempt to protect his naked body, Ackland rained blow after blow on to the lid until it was demolished.

Flinging aside his shotgun, he pulled him down on to the floor and began tearing the bandage from his head.

The face which was finally revealed was almost identical to that of the man who had been brought to them in the aquarium, except the skin was as wrinkled as a crab-apple and the teeth worn and yellow with age.

Panting, Ackland looked up. 'Is this him?'

'That's him.'

Taking a deep breath, Ackland hoisted Snaith to his feet and began fumbling for his handcuffs. 'What's the time now, for chrissakes?' he asked.

Fitzpatrick shone the flashlight on to his wristwatch, then put it to his ear for a moment. 'That's odd,' he replied, his eyes on Snaith. 'It's just stopped . . .'

34

Forrestal pushed back the cuff of his silk shirt and touched a button on his digital wristwatch. 'What the hell's taking them so long,' he asked peevishly.

It was now 10.25, and the returning Buffalo had been expected to touch down at Homestead Air Force Base at a little before 10.00. However, it was not the fact that it was overdue that was worrying the Attorney-General and the men in the crowded control tower. Not even Forrestal had expected airline scheduling – there were just too many imponderables. The eye might have been late arriving at Hippocrates Cay. Or it might have been wider than had been forecast, or slower moving, giving the assault squad more time on the island than had been thought possible.

Nevertheless they had expected – long before now – to have been in radio contact. Yet try as they might, they had not been able to raise the Buffalo, nor see any sign of it on their radar scopes.

Forrestal reached into the pocket of his black Yves St Laurent trench coat and looked again at the schedule for that day. How the hell were they, he wondered, going to get through everything when they were already so far behind their timelines?

As soon as the Buffalo landed, he and a team of intelligence experts planned to de-brief the crew and every member of the assault squad. Once they knew precisely what had happened during the mission the President would be told, and work begun on the final updates to the speech he would broadcast early that evening – one of a batch prepared to cover every degree of success or failure.

Then, assuming the mission was deemed a success, there would be a short ceremony during which the President would telephone his congratulations to the pilots and the assault commander.

Immediately following the ceremony several things would happen simultaneously. An ambulance would take Clair Tennant to a specially prepared suite in the base hospital (where any of the wounded would already have been taken), and Snaith and the other prisoners would be smuggled into the Police Headquarters Building in Miami, where they would be formally charged. Forrestal would then return to Washington in an aircraft specially equipped as a film-processing laboratory and newsroom. During the four-hour flight, FBI darkroom technicians would process and print all of the photographs taken during and after the mission, and Forrestal and the Director of the International Communication Agency would select those pictures which – together with a detailed account of the mission – would be released to the wire services of the world the moment the President came off the air at 7.15 Eastern Standard Time.

Forrestal waved aside the offer of coffee and looked again at his watch. It was now 10.35, and there was still no sign of the overdue Buffalo.

Suddenly he stopped worrying about whether or not it had crashed, and began worrying about *where* it might have crashed. The more he thought about the possibilities, the more he began to hope that either it had never arrived at Hippocrates Cay, or that it had disintegrated over open sea on its way back from the island.

He sprang to his feet and began pacing up and down. If only he could establish that the aircraft *had* been lost, that would at least be something. Then he could let the President know he would have to go on the air with his standby speech about the energy crisis, while he, Forrestal, began doing something about losing the whole operation between the radiator and the wall.

'Christ Almighty!' he suddenly cried. 'Isn't there something somebody can do to find out what the hell's happened?'

'We're doing everything possible,' said Colonel Gestler, the commanding officer of the base.

'Except actually *look* for them.'

'But we *are* looking for them!' Gestler protested, waving at the row of radar scopes. Like everyone else on the base who'd had any dealings with Forrestal, he had grown to loathe the man.

'I mean get up off your asses and go *out* there and look for them.'

'If it's a search you're asking for, forget it,' said Gestler, walking away to get on with something more useful. 'Mounting a search'll be impossible until Hilda's out of the area.'

One of the telephones in the control room had begun ringing, and was answered by the chief duty officer. 'It's for you, Mr General,' he told Forrestal. 'The President.'

Grim-faced, he strode across and snatched the phone from the man's hand. 'It's not looking good, Mr President,' the others heard him say. 'I'm doing all I can, but I'm just not getting the co-operation at this end of the line I'd hoped for.'

While he was explaining the situation to the President, Gestler slipped across to another of the phones and dialled a number. 'Listen,' he began, speaking quietly and with his back to the Attorney-General. 'I'm getting a lot of flak from you-know-who. It's beginning to look like we've lost SAM Zero One. I'm afraid so. What I want you to do is get on the horn to every Coast Guard Station between Savannah and San Juan, okay? I *know* New York's already asked them to keep watch, but let's make sure nobody's sleeping on the job, huh?'

Gestler rang off just in time to hear Forrestal say: 'You mustn't blame yourself for any of this, Mr President. No, I'm not going to say I told you so. Although, as you know, I was never happy about this mission, I didn't expect it to end this way.'

He handed the telephone back to the duty officer and turned to Gestler. 'I guess somebody had better put Lippencott in the picture,' he said. He seemed to have forgotten all about the idea of starting a search. 'Where is he right now?'

Gestler explained that he was waiting in his office.

Forrestal nodded. 'That's where I'll be for the next ten minutes.'

When Forrestal arrived at Gestler's office, Lippencott was standing staring aimlessly out at the rain-swept parking ramps and hangars. He had slept badly the previous night, and was looking pale and exhausted.

Forrestal explained the situation to him, as he had to the President. 'Now this doesn't mean, of course, that there's any reason to suppose that Miss Tennant or Mr Fitzpatrick – assuming he was on the island – have necessarily been lost along with the others,' he added. 'It could be that the assault squad never made it to the island.'

'How many guys were there in the squad?'

'Twenty-two, including the pilots.'

'Jeez!' Lippencott pulled a long face.

'Ed – may I call you Ed? – I guess this is as good a time as any to thank you for all you've done.'

Faintly embarrassed, Lippencott began protesting that he had done nothing, but Forrestal stopped him. 'You have. Believe me, you really have. And let me tell you something else – the President's very grateful. Without your co-operation in keeping this whole thing under wraps, he'd never have been able to get Witch-finder off the ground.'

'The way it's turned out, I'm beginning to wish I *hadn't* gone along with keeping it under wraps . . .'

Forrestal nodded gravely. 'I guess we all feel a bit like that right now. I know I wish I'd tried harder to persuade him not to go this route. Still, we mustn't be too tough on ourselves, nor on him. It couldn't have been an easy decision to take . . .' Suddenly brightening, he gripped Lippencott's elbow and gave him a politician's handshake. 'Ed, it's been nice knowing you. And listen, if there's anything I can ever do for you, don't hesitate to call my office, y'heah.'

'Well, what's the situation?' Forrestal demanded, as soon as he was back in the tower.

'I'm afraid it isn't good,' Gestler replied gravely. 'We've just had a call from the Coast Guard at Miami. The captain of a tanker in the Florida Straits has reported seeing what might have been a mid-air explosion to the east.

'Of course, it *could* have been lightning, and anyway, until we've found identifiable wreckage we won't know for—'

He broke off, his attention taken by a sudden flurry of activity in front of the radar scopes.

'What's happening?' he called across to the watch supervisor.

'We've picked up something that could *just* be SAM Zero One,' he answered. 'There sure as hell shouldn't be anything else flying in that area – not with Hilda just over the horizon . . .'

Forrestal crossed the floor and pushed his way into the crowd that had begun to gather behind the radar operator and his supervisor. 'I can't see anything!' he said, resentfully.

The watch supervisor agreed that, with Hilda causing so much interference, it wasn't easy to see the blip. 'But it's there,' he insisted. 'It's there all right . . .'

'But if it *is* them, why aren't they answering your calls?'

'I guess their radio must be out of action,' replied the watch supervisor. 'They may have taken a lightning strike. If that's happened it could also have screwed up their compass – which would explain why they're off course . . .'

A telephone began ringing. The duty officer picked it up, listened for a moment, then put his hand over the mouthpiece.

'Gentlemen,' he said, loud enough for the whole room to hear. 'I've got the Miami Coast Guard on the line again – they've just spotted SAM Zero One! She's coming in at 5,000 feet. One of her engines appears to be dead, but otherwise—'

A great cheer went up from the men in the room, drowning the end of the duty officer's sentence.

35

The President began turning over the photographs which the Director of the International Communication Agency had just brought across from Andrews Air Force Base.

'So this is our Dr Snaith, is it?' he said, looking at a picture of a scowling, barefoot man wrapped in a blanket. 'Hell, he actually *looks* like a blood-drinker!'

The next picture was of a young man with his arm around the shoulders of a pretty girl in a dressing-gown. Although her face was stained with tears, she looked radiantly happy.

'I guess this *has* to be Clair Tennant,' said the President. 'Who's the guy with her?'

'Her boyfriend – Michael Fitzpatrick.'

'I've been meaning to ask all afternoon – just what *did* happen to that son-of-a-gun?'

'What *didn't* happen to him!' said the Director, in an awed voice. 'Y'know, Mr President, he damned nearly succeeded with that crazy stunt of his. After he got ashore, he dragged Snaith and his Bahamian mistress out of bed, took them at gunpoint to the helipad—'

'But I was told his gun was found aboard the *Marlowe* . . .'

'That's right, it was. After they captured Fitzpatrick, they put everything back to make it look as if he'd never gotten to the island.

'Anyway,' continued the Director, 'before they left the villa, Snaith had ordered Clair to be released and the chopper started up. But then, when he realized Fitzpatrick intended taking *him* back to Miami, he announced that if he tried, the chopper would be shot down. It seems he preferred to get it over with here and then rather than face spending the remainder of his life on Death Row.'

'Was he serious?' asked the President.

'Fitzpatrick thought so, specially since he'd noticed that some of the guards were carrying ground-to-air missile launchers.'

'So what did he do?'

'Well, he knew that having the coloured girl on board was no guarantee that they wouldn't be shot to hell as soon as Snaith had been released. So he did a deal: he offered to stay behind while the chopper took Snaith, the coloured girl and Clair – riding shotgun – first to Abaco, where Snaith would have been put off, and from there to Miami. Then, when Snaith was safely back on Hippocrates Cay, Fitzpatrick would have been exchanged for the coloured girl. Or at least, that was the idea.'

'Sounds a good one,' said the President. 'So, what went wrong?'

'When Clair finally arrived at the helipad and saw Fitzpatrick, she broke away from her guards and started running towards him.'

'Jeez-*us*!' said the President.

The Director shrugged. 'I know – it was a pretty dumb thing to have done. Still, I guess you can't blame the poor kid too much; she probably didn't know what the hell was happening, and anyway, from where she was she apparently couldn't see he had a gun to Snaith's head.

'Fitzpatrick yelled for her to stay back, but she couldn't hear him because of the helicopter engines.

'It was just what the guards had been waiting for. One of them brought Snaith down with a football tackle, and Fitzpatrick took an M-16 round in the shoulder.'

'It's quite a story,' said the President, examining the photograph of Fitzpatrick and Clair at arm's length. 'Y'know something? While we've been talking I've been thinking; this picture—' he turned it around so that the others could see '—this picture could do more to justify Witch-finder in the minds of Mr and Mrs America than anything! *This* – this is what Witch-finder has been all about, right?'

The Director of the International Communication Agency agreed. 'From an image point of view, we've been lucky all the way along the line,' he said. 'The girl's a honey – in fact, they make a good-looking couple – the assault commander photographs like he stepped straight out of a Marlboro ad—'

'And I see you even got yourselves a black co-opilot,' said the President's press secretary. 'Pity it couldn't have been a black *woman* co-pilot, but I guess you can't have everything.'

The President passed him the photograph. 'Listen, I wouldn't mind having this on the table beside me when I'm on TV. Use it as a kind of – as a kind of a logo, y'know what I mean?'

The President checked himself in the make-up girl's hand mirror. Wearing a white open-necked shirt and a white, heavy-knit cardigan had, he decided, been a very good idea. Not only would the garments themselves help lend an air of confident informality to the occasion, but white – as well as flattering his tan – was a colour traditionally associated with the good guys.

'Where would you like this, sir?' asked the chief usher, holding up the now framed photograph of Fitzpatrick and Clair.

'Right there,' replied the President, pointing to a table along-side the easy chair in which he would be sitting during trans-mission. 'I guess we're still going to be able to see the books, aren't we?' The President was proud of his reputation for being an avid reader.

A member of the TV camera crew assured him that the viewers would still be able to see that he was sitting in front of a bookcase. 'Just don't be tempted to pick up the photograph while we're on the air,' he warned. 'We could get flare off the glass.'

The library door opened and the President's appointments secretary picked her way through the forest of lights and cameras. 'Attorney-General Forrestal's just arrived,' she announced.

The President beamed. 'Fantastic!' Although he had talked on the telephone to Forrestal many times during the day, he had not expected to see him until later that evening. 'Have him come up.'

'He says he has to speak with you alone, Mr President.'

'Is something the matter?'

The appointments secretary made sure they could not be overheard. 'I think there may be.'

The President found the Attorney-General in the Oval Office, staring through the French windows overlooking the Rose Garden, his hands thrust deep in the pockets of his black trench coat.

'Hank!' he said warmly. 'Hank, it's good to see you. Take off your coat, and I'll have them get you a cup of coffee.'

Forrestal shook his head. 'There isn't time, Mr President. Listen, I've just got through with talking to Schneider in Miami—'

'Schneider? Who's Schneider?'

'The President of the National Academy of Sciences!' Forrestal explained, irritated that he should have forgotten. 'You remember, he's one of the guys who've been carrying out a spot evaluation of the scientific evidence.

'Anyway, to come straight to the point, Schneider's as worried as all hell about how the public might react to what Snaith's been doing. He thinks that with a growing movement of irrationalism in this country, it could trigger a wave of anti-science feeling so strong that a lot of the work going on right now'll be stopped dead in its tracks!'

The President looked baffled. 'Hank, I'm sorry, but I'm just not with you . . .'

'Okay, but we haven't got much time,' said Forrestal. 'Look, during the past few years a helluva lot of people – and I'm talking about your Mr Average Joe, not just a bunch of hippies and weirdos – have become paranoid about science. They see nuclear reactors as – well I guess as some kind of Frankenstein monster, not as a cheap source of power in a world fast running out of fossil fuels. For them, genetic engineering is a potential health hazard, not a vital tool in the search for a cure for cancer; automation, a threat to their livelihoods; insecticides—'

The President held up his hands. 'I get the message. But what's all this to do with Snaith?'

'I was just coming to that. Snaith's a scientist, right? And Snaith's done a lot of things your Mr Average Joe's always been afraid scientists would get around to doing sooner or later: the sonuvabitch has been fooling around with brain transplants, test-tube babies, clones, man-animal hybrids—' He paused

244

That's another thing; Schneider's afraid that some of the hybrids might have escaped into the sea when the lab collapsed. If they did, and the bastards breed, we could have the same problem with them as we're having with killer bees, only ten thousand times worse.'

The President shrugged. 'So get the Navy on the job,' he said. 'Have them mount a search and destroy mission.'

'They're working on it right now. But that's not the point,' continued Forrestal. 'The point is that if Snaith's capable of doing all that on an island in the *Bahamas*, for chrissake, what're they capable of doing at MIT, Stanford, Cal Tec, Cornell—'

'*Hank*!' The President began to chuckle. 'Hank, listen. Snaith was only able to do what he did because he *wasn't* at Cal Tec or Cornell!'

'Okay, but just you try explaining that when they start picking the campuses and the defence establishments . . .

'Anyway, that isn't the worst part. According to Schneider's people, when the dust has finally settled this country's going to be facing a revolution of expectations that'll knock it sideways!'

'I don't understand,' said the President curtly.

Forrestal hesitated for a moment, not quite sure where best to begin. 'Look, we're committed to a programme of socialized medicine, right? Okay, so what happens when it becomes known that the technology exists to grow rejection-proof organs? I'll tell you; every sonuvabitch who needs one is going to demand one as of right!

'Mr President, if we grew a new heart for everyone who needed it – and I'm just talking about *hearts* now – we'd end up doing 100,000 transplants a year! Then there'd be *kidney* transplants, and right now there's thought to be something like nine million people suffering from kidney disease in the US; *liver* transplants; *pancreas* transplants—'

'So what? If people need them and we can give them to 'em, why shouldn't they have them?'

'Do you have any idea what all of that would cost?' demanded Forrestal. 'Mr President, we're talking about high-technology medicine on an un*precedented* scale. If we were suddenly

245

expected to provide a transplants-to-order service as part of our socialized medicine programme, it would cost us hundred of billions of dollars annually.

'And there's another thing; even if we could find the money the cost-benefit figures on this deal don't make any kind of sense. Christ, with automation catching on the way it is, we've already got more people than we know what to do with!'

'What you seem to be asking me to do,' said the President 'is block medical progress, right? Okay, well let me ask you something: what would have happened if some guy had decided it wasn't a good idea for people to be immunized, or allowed antibiotics?'

'For one thing, we wouldn't now be facing the prospect of world so over-populated that by the end of the next century there's likely to be standing room only!' Forrestal picked up replica of Harry Truman's desk plaque lettered THE BUCK STOP HERE and began tapping it against the side of his leg. 'Look don't get me wrong, I'm not saying that we shouldn't *ever* have transplants-to-order,' he continued in a more conciliatory tone 'All I'm saying is that we should keep it under wraps until we know whether we can handle it or not. Christ, we're having enough problems with this socialized medicine deal as it is!'

'So, what do you suggest we do?'

'Try coming to an accommodation with Snaith's attorney We don't indict him for murder, in return for which he plead guilty to a handful of lesser charges – illegal practice, tax evasion. Something along those lines.'

The President looked at him as if he was mad. 'Hank, for crying out loud! We fly troops in through a hurricane and violate another country's sovereignty in order to bring a guy back to stand trial for *tax evasion*?'

'Okay.' Forrestal shrugged. 'So maybe we'll have to add un lawful flight or even kidnapping to the cake-mix. But it's still helluva lot better deal from Snaith's point of view than Murder One. And that way, we don't have to raise any aspects the case we don't want raised.'

The President shook his head. 'No way!' he said grim 'From the beginning, this has been an open Administratio and that's the way it's going to—'

'Mr President,' Forrestal interjected, 'there just isn't time for the Gettysburg Address. I'm sorry, but we're really behind the eight-ball on this thing.'

'It doesn't matter. There's still no way you're going to persuade me to start monkeying around with the due processes. Goddammit, Hank, after what happened to Nixon I'm surprised you even tried. Surprised and disappointed. Very disappointed.'

'Is that your final word?'

'It most certainly is!'

With a show of reluctance, Forrestal produced a sheaf of papers from his pocket and thrust them into the President's hand. 'In that case, you'd better take a look at this . . .'

'What is it?' he asked, crossing to his desk for a pair of spectacles.

'A list of Snaith's former patients. It's just come through on the wire from Miami.'

The President began reading. 'I'll be damned!' he chuckled. 'Wait till the Chairman of the Republican Party hears about *this*!'

'Go on . . .'

Greedily, the President turned to the next sheet. Half-way down the list he suddenly looked up. 'Who's the guy with the same name as my brother?'

'Mr President, it *is* your brother!' Forrestal took a rolled-up 10 x 8 photoprint from his other pocket and handed it to him. 'I'm sorry, but they've found a video-tape of the actual operation. Snaith used to say he was having them made for teaching purposes, but their real function was as a form of insurance. I had our people in Miami run your brother's tape, photograph the best close-up and put it on the wire to me. I'm afraid there's absolutely no doubt who the patient is . . .'

The President's face had gone white under his TV make-up. 'But this is crazy,' he said. 'When the hell was he supposed to have *had* the operation?'

'A couple of years back. We've checked the newspaper clips, and the story at the time was that he'd gone into hospital for what most of them described as "minor surgery".'

'That's right. He had a hernia . . .'

Forrestal shook his head. 'He had a kidney transplant. Okay, so maybe he didn't know his donor would be murdered by Snaith. Maybe he thought he was just buying himself a place at the head of the line. But that's not going to help him – or you – if it gets out.'

The President crossed to the window behind his desk, and for almost a minute stood staring out through the green-tinted bullet-proof glass at the Washington Monument. The light was draining away fast, and it had begun to rain. With his back to the room he asked: 'If we *were* to do some kind of a deal with Snaith, how would we keep the lid on the story? Surely to Christ, too many people already know what he's been up to?'

'Not all that many when you think about it. The guys who've been evaluating the scientific evidence *want* it suppressed, so they're no problem. Neither is the Bureau, as long as they get a conviction.'

'But there's the Rangers! What about the Rangers?'

'Only Ackland and maybe three or four of the others actually saw what had been going on,' replied Forrestal. 'And it shouldn't be too much of a problem to take care of them.'

The President turned to give him a hard, dull look. 'Are you suggesting what I think you're suggesting?'

Forrestal sighed. 'I'm sorry, Mr President, but it's no good us being candy-assed about this thing. There's just too much at stake.'

'But what about Fitzpatrick and Tennant? Hank, they're not even American *citizens*! Are you suggesting we should – that we should take care of them too?'

'Fitzpatrick's no problem. He's already dead.'

The President's mouth sagged open. 'I don't believe it!'

'Officially, at least. He was posted as dead after they found the *Marlowe* abandoned. Hell, there's even been a memorial service for him at some church in Fleet Street.'

'Hank, he'll have *called* someone by now – his folks, or his paper – to let them know he's still in one piece!'

Forrestal shook his head. 'Everyone connected with the mission's being held incommunicado until you come off the air at 7.15. It was the only way we could be sure there would be no leaks.'

'All right, but there's the girl. What about the girl?'

'Well, I guess we could always ask Teddy Kennedy to drive her home,' replied Forrestal with a wry smile.

The President's eyes flashed angrily. 'Hank, for God's *sake*!'

'I'm sorry.' Forrestal began again. 'Look, I know this may seem a bit far out, but supposing we give her to Mancini?'

'Give her to *Mancini*? What the hell are you talking about?'

'Well, we're going to have to find *some* way of keeping the sonuvabitch quiet. Thanks to Snaith, he's down two million bucks and he still hasn't had his transplant. So, if he sees Snaith being allowed to get away with it, he's going to be hopping mad. And if that happens, we're *really* in trouble!'

'Why not have him taken care of along with the others?'

The President's irony was lost on Forrestal. 'Too difficult. Look, we know Tennant's heart was hand-picked for Mancini. So in return for having him keep his mouth shut, we let him have it. All wrapped up in pink ribbons and with a get-well-soon card. Hell, we can even make it easy for him by saying she hit her head during the flight back!'

'But why can't we have Snaith *grow* him a heart? Why does it have to be the girl's?'

'For one thing, Snaith's going to be in custody. And for another, if we're going to batten down the hatches on this transplant-to-order thing, there must be no exceptions.'

'Hold it a minute!' said the President, pressing his fingertips against his greying temples. 'Look, I'm light years away from being convinced that we need to do anything remotely like this. But if in the end we're forced – absolutely forced to resort to such measures, why don't we have something happen to *Snaith*? Hell, if Snaith wasn't around to stand trial, our troubles would be over, wouldn't they?'

Forrestal shook his head. 'Forget about eliminating Snaith. It's just not on.'

'Why not?'

'For the same reason it wasn't on to eliminate Philip Agee and Victor Marchetti when they began embarrassing the shit out of the CIA back in the mid-'70s – it's just too damned obvious. Can you *imagine* the stink that would be raised if Snaith died while in police custody?'

'But what about the stink that's going to be raised when it's discovered that half-a-dozen of our key witnesses have died?' demanded the President.

'Three times that number died following the assassination of Jack Kennedy, and I don't remember it exactly bringing down the government!'

The President sat down at his desk and buried his head in his hands.

'Of course, if you do it my way it'll mean taking some of the heat out of this,' continued Forrestal, flicking through the text of the President's speech. 'But I reckon that could be done by simply cutting from "The distinguished statesman Benjamin Disraeli once said that justice was truth in action" bla, bla, bla, through to "It was for this reason that Attorney-General Forrestal, with my full knowledge and approval, did what had to be done, no more and no less, to ensure that these charges would not go unanswered". It still makes sense, and we'd have gotten rid of any mention of what the charges were to have been.'

Forrestal tossed the text on to the desk. 'It'll mean you having to read from that and not the TelePrompter, and you'd have to slow down on your delivery if you're to avoid underrunning. But apart from that there're no problems.

'Okay, I realize the uncut version's already gone out as a briefing document to all our embassies, but that shouldn't be too tough to handle,' he added. 'We just tell 'em that after examining the physical evidence we had to reduce the charges against Snaith or risk losing the bastard completely.'

The President looked up; he seemed to have aged ten years during the past few minutes. 'But the press release! What about the press release?'

'I put a stop on that before I came over here.' Forrestal glanced at his wristwatch. 'You're on the air in six minutes,' he announced. 'Now, what're you going to do?'

Wearily, the President reached out for the text of his speech. 'What was that cut you suggested I make?' he asked.

Forrestal breathed a sigh of relief. 'I know it was a tough decision to take, Mr President. But believe me, we've looked at

250

this situation every whichway, and we're all agreed that sanitizing it is the only viable option open to us.'

'Now wait a *minute*!' said the President, indignantly. 'Let's get one thing straight; all I'm doing is buying a little *time*. Time in which to try and come up with a solution that doesn't involve the death of innocent people.'

A light on his telephone console began flashing, and he snatched up the handset. 'Yes?'

He listened for a moment – his blank, red-rimmed eyes on the Attorney-General – and then said: 'Tell them I'll be right through.

'Oh, and also tell them to kill the picture of the couple,' he added. 'I shan't be needing the picture of the couple.'

Afterword

Since completing the outline for *Side-effect* in the spring of 1976, certain of the elements of the story, which at that time were entirely fictional, have become fact.

The first such transformation occurred when Israel mounted a military operation to rescue hostages from Entebbe Airport. This was followed by the election of an American president who had made health one of the planks in his campaign; the publication of a book describing the cloning of a human being; the birth of the world's first test-tube baby; the issuing of guidelines for a national health care programme in America; the re-emergence of gun control as an issue in American politics; the ending of a five-year ban on heart transplants in Britain; and the opening, again in Britain, of a tissue-matching laboratory with a computer on which is stored data concerning prospective transplant *donors* (name and location of laboratory deleted from manuscript).

Furthermore, it is a fact that:

● Unethical medical experiments have been performed on human beings, the most notorious of which were by doctors in Nazi concentration camps during World War II. However, there have been more recent examples of what are, at best, ethically doubtful medical experiments. One such case involved injecting the inmates of Willowbrook, a residential school for mentally defective children in New York State, with live hepatitis virus. Writing about the case in the *Dictionary of Medical Ethics* (Darton, Longman & Todd, 1977), Owen L. Wade, Professor of Therapeutics and Clinical Pharmacology, University of Birmingham, said:

Because most children admitted to the hospital became infected [with hepatitis], the medical staff felt justified in giving the children hepatitis virus and isolating them in a special unit so that the were at less risk. It is claimed that this policy, possibly justified when it was started in 1956, was continued because the medical staff wished to carry on their research on hepatitis, *and new measures which might give protection to children from infective hepatitis were not used* [my italics].

And at the Jewish Chronic Disease Hospital, Brooklyn, doctors from the Sloan-Kettering Cancer Research Institute injected nineteen patients suffering from chronic debilitating diseases with live cancer cells (*Science*, 1966, **151**, 636). In his deeply disturbing book *Human Guinea Pigs: Experimentation on Man* (Routledge & Kegan Paul, 1967), Dr M. H. Pappworth had this to say about the Brooklyn case:

> The doctors who carried out the experiment agreed that there was no written consent, but maintained that the patients had been verbally informed that this was a cancer experiment and that the injections might produce localized lumps. *But it was acknowledged that the patients had not been informed that the injections consisted of live cancer cells* [my italics], as it was felt, according to a spokesman, that imparting such knowledge would adversely affect the patients' emotional and physical condition.

Such cases are by no means restricted to America. To quote again from the *Dictionary of Medical Ethics*:

> The temptation to carry out a non-therapeutic investigation without a full explanation or even any explanation at all is always very strong. In some European countries it is often assumed that it is unlikely that the patient or the parent will co-operate and neither formal permission nor co-operation is sought.

● Two Nobel laureates, the biologist Jean Rostand and the geneticist Joshua Lederberg, have suggested that cloning might one day be used as a means of providing rejection-proof organs or transplantation. Although controversy still surrounds the claim made by science reporter David Rorvik that a human being has been cloned (*In His Image: the Cloning of a Man*, Hamish Hamilton, 1978), the cloning of animals was first achieved by Dr J. B. Gurdon at Oxford University in 1960.

● Artificial wombs already exist. At Johns Hopkins University, Dr Yu-Chih Hsu has grown mice embryos to the heartbeat stage *in vitro*. The first claim to have grown a human foetus *in vitro* was made in 1959 by Dr Daniele Petrucci of the University of Bologna (following protests by the Vatican, Petrucci is said to have terminated his experiment – an act which, incidentally, led to demands that he be tried for murder).

● Cephalic transplants (the grafting of the head of one animal on to the decapitated body of another) have already been performed, notably by Professor Robert J. White at the Neurosurgical Research Laboratories of the Cleveland Metropolitan General Hospital.

● Experiments involving the fusion of human cells and animal cells have been carried out in laboratories throughout the world, and, at the Brookhaven National Laboratory, scientists have fused human cells and plant cells.

● Experiments in the use of plants as stress alarm indicators were carried out by the US Army at Fort Belvoir, Virginia.

● The question of cost effectiveness in medicine is not new. Following the first three British heart transplants, Sir George Godber, chief medical officer of what was then the Ministry of Health, chaired a meeting of the country's foremost medical experts at which it was decided that the status of heart transplantation was such as not to justify 'diverting resources which could be used more productively for other work in the health service' (quoted in 'Ten years of heart transplants' by Roger Maynard, *Listener*, 3rd August 1978). And according to the distinguished medical researcher Donald Longmore (himself a member of the surgical team which performed the first British heart transplant in 1968), the issue of cost effectiveness in medicine is likely to become more, not less, acute in the future. In *Spare-Part Surgery: The Surgical Practice of the Future* (Doubleday, 1968), Donald Longmore had this to say:

The pace of medical advance has been so brisk and so accelerated that, if the best current methods of diagnosis, treatment, alleviation, healing, life-support, and preventive medicine were universally and impartially applied in even the wealthiest countries, the cost could soak up a good proportion of the gross national product (GNP). In the not-too-distant future these potential costs might even *exceed* the GNP. The medical profession itself has hardly grasped what this implies. It means that, just as we now accept that certain diseases and conditions are beyond our present powers of healing, so we may one day have to accept that it is beyond our economic power to provide the best and latest facilities, and the staff to run them . . .

● Attempts have been made to organize a Unilateral Declaration of Independence on behalf of the inhabitants of Abaco, notably by a consortium of American businessmen led by the arms dealer Mitchell Livingston Werbell.

● The Los Angeles Police Department – along with a number of other American law-enforcement agencies – does have a hypnosis squad, and the Central Intelligence Agency did fund considerable research into the use of mind-control techniques, including hypnosis and the non-clinical application of ECT.

● Computer crime is now so common that in 1978 the Institution of Electrical Engineers was able to publish a bibliography containing the titles of no less than seventy books and articles devoted exclusively to the subject.

Raymond Hawkey

London
October, 1979.

NEL BESTSELLERS

T046 133	HOW GREEN WAS MY VALLEY	*Richard Llewellyn*	£1.00
T039 560	I BOUGHT A MOUNTAIN	*Thomas Firbank*	95p
T033 988	IN THE TEETH OF THE EVIDENCE	*Dorothy L. Sayers*	90p
T038 149	THE CARPETBAGGERS	*Harold Robbins*	£1.50
T040 917	TO SIR WITH LOVE	*E.R. Braithwaite*	75p
T041 719	HOW TO LIVE WITH A NEUROTIC DOG	*Stephen Baker*	75p
T040 925	THE PRIZE	*Irving Wallace*	£1.65
T034 755	THE CITADEL	*A.J. Cronin*	£1.10
T042 189	STRANGER IN A STRANGE LAND	*Robert Heinlein*	£1.25
T037 053	79 PARK AVENUE	*Harold Robbins*	£1.25
T042 308	DUNE	*Frank Herbert*	£1.50
T045 137	THE MOON IS A HARSH MISTRESS	*Robert Heinlein*	£1.25
T040 933	THE SEVEN MINUTES	*Irving Wallace*	£1.50
T038 130	THE INHERITORS	*Harold Robbins*	£1.25
T035 689	RICH MAN, POOR MAN	*Irwin Shaw*	£1.50
T037 134	EDGE 27: DEATH DRIVE	*George G. Gilman*	75p
T037 541	DEVIL'S GUARD	*Robert Elford*	£1.25
T042 774	THE RATS	*James Herbert*	80p
T042 340	CARRIE	*Stephen King*	80p
T042 782	THE FOG	*James Herbert*	90p
T033 740	THE MIXED BLESSING	*Helen Van Slyke*	£1.25
T037 061	BLOOD AND MONEY	*Thomas Thompson*	£1.50
T038 629	THIN AIR	*Simpson & Burger*	95p
T038 602	THE APOCALYPSE	*Jeffrey Konvitz*	95p

NEL P.O. BOX 11, FALMOUTH TR10 9EN, CORNWALL

Postage charge:

U.K. Customers. Please allow 25p for the first book plus 10p per copy for each additional book ordered to a maximum charge of £1.05 to cover the cost of postage and packing, in addition to cover price.

B.F.P.O. & Eire. Please allow 25p for the first book plus 10p per copy for the next 8 books, thereafter 5p per book, in addition to cover price.

Overseas Customers. Please allow 40p for the first book plus 12p per copy for each additional book, in addition to cover price.

Please send cheque or postal order (no currency).

Name ....

Address ....

....

Title ....

While every effort is made to keep prices steady, it is sometimes necessary to increase prices at short notice. New English Library reserve the right to show on covers and charge new retail prices which may differ from those advertised in the text or elsewhere.